agribusiness
agricultural machin...
agronomy
animal & p...
farm mech...
floriculture
food processing
horticulture
landscaping
off-farm agricultural occupations

Agricultural Education

THE LIBRARY OF EDUCATION

A Project of The Center for Applied Research in Education, Inc.

Categories of Coverage

I	II	III
Curriculum and Teaching	Administration, Organization, and Finance	Psychology for Educators

IV	V	VI
History, Philosophy, and Social Foundations	Professional Skills	Educational Institutions

Agricultural Education

GLENN Z. STEVENS

Professor of Agricultural Education
The Pennsylvania State University

The Center for Applied Research in Education, Inc.
New York

LIBRARY OF CONGRESS
CATALOG CARD NO.: 67–23315

PRINTED IN THE UNITED STATES OF AMERICA

Foreword

There is a community of scholarship between the natural science of agriculture and the behavioral science of education. Both agriculture and education are applied sciences. The evidence of their value is their record of rewarding application. It is clear that the author believes that this area of scholarship is worth the effort—worth his as a commentator and worth ours as inquirers. The book is a description of the contemporary stage of a highly successful experiment in creating a development model. The emphasis of the model is on human resources and the context is the rural environment. The assumption is that there is intrinsic merit in a focus which combines this emphasis and this context. The assumption does not need a defense. In the first place, any alternative would restrict opportunity and thus would be inimical to our interpretation of justice. Secondly, the most common occupation of agriculture, namely farming, is the largest single occupational category whose practitioners have limited access to systematic formalized occupational education. Thus, any development model operating in this milieu is relatively rare and its success mechanisms will repay the most careful, scholarly inquiry.

It is obvious that this book is a systematic, constructive assessment of the field of agricultural education. It is not impressionistic. It is also obvious that the author is a dedicated teacher who has learned that one cannot change the mind of others without changing one's own. Most of all it is clear that the book has been written by a critic whose intellectual tolerance does not extend to fashions or fads whose claims for existence rest on currency alone. It is based on principles and on the illustrations of them.

There is a quality of timeliness in this book which appeals to the general reader as well as to those with special interests in agricultural education. Professor Stevens examines an educational process likely to contain the necessary ingredients for the solution of the problem of world food supply. The absence of such ingredients will find increasing millions of people bereft of hope and countless more whose future cannot be otherwise. The book deals with common concerns rather than with parochial problems and with major issues rather than with side arguments. Thus there is increased likelihood that it does, in fact, contain many of the ingredients which may provide solutions to the problems of world-wide human condition.

Finally, it should be said that the author has that unusual quality of making the simple sound exciting and making the complex sound simple. His expositions will fill a gap with admirable clarity. They are appropriate to the present state of the art and to the stages just ahead. They are worth the effort—both his and ours.

GORDON I. SWANSON

Coordinator, International Programs
College of Education
University of Minnesota

Agricultural Education

Glenn Z. Stevens

Professor Glenn Z. Stevens has written a very fine book on a topic of considerable significance, Agricultural Education. One wonders how such a thorough coverage of the subject could be accomplished in the short format of the Library of Education, yet this has been accomplished by writing in a clear and concise manner. The style was possible only because the author has such a complete knowledge of the field.

Agricultural Education first presents a discussion of the scope and organization of vocational-technical education in agriculture. This is followed by chapters on objectives, curriculum and courses of study, teaching high school students, and the education of adults. Stevens concludes with discussions of instructional resources and of the administration and supervision of the program. There is a short bibliography.

This book should have particular significance to students of education in general, in addition to those specifically concerned with agriculture. Probably no other area of education has reached the high level of excellence in the attainment of goals and in organization to achieve these goals as has agricultural education. Based upon sound research, with well-trained teachers and carefully prepared materials, agricultural education has trained generations of farmers to be the best in the world. The philosophy and techniques of the movement should be studied carefully and emulated by others in the field of general education. The model might, however, be even more carefully studied by such special fields as vocational education.

Dr. Glenn Z. Stevens is Professor of Agricultural Education at The Pennsylvania State University.

DANIEL E. GRIFFITHS

Content Editor

Contents

CHAPTER VIII

Teacher Education, Research, and Evaluation   100

CHAPTER I

Organization and Scope of Vocational-Technical Education in Agriculture

Agriculture is an integral part of the total program of instruction in ten thousand comprehensive high schools and area vocational-technical schools in the United States. It is education in agriculture for the specific purpose of contributing to the occupational development of each student. It is education that is relevant to personal achievement of economic goals. Agricultural education is meaningful also in the general education of high school students and adults.

Occupational education is changing rapidly. Emphasis on the relation of school and work is increasing. To prepare to make the many decisions that shape the development of their individual careers, high school boys and girls need specific guidance. They can learn much about modern business and professional employment by taking elective courses in vocational education fields.

In a large proportion of American families one or more adults is involved to some degree in activities that use knowledge and abilities in agricultural science. Food and other products of the commercial farms of the United States are produced in adequate quantity by owner-operators and employees highly trained in specific technologies. Market quality advances steadily, and sometimes almost spectacularly, as scientific research is combined with automation to give consumers greater variety and convenience in attractive, desirable goods at competitive prices.

Expansion in the industrial economy and an increase in services that provide employment for many persons formerly confined to a subsistence way of life in rural areas represent healthy changes. The transition has in recent years called forth a justifiable demand that appropriate industrial education and education for the many new types of service occupations be made accessible to rural youth and adults. Area vocational-technical high schools are being built. Post-high school technician education is being provided in several types of institutions.

1

Vocational education in agriculture for farming occupations has been conducted successfully in comprehensive high schools in communities where many families engage in commercial agricultural production. It is expected that the programs will be continued. The emerging needs for new courses are in specialized fields of off-farm agricultural business and industry. Efficient organization of instruction at appropriate levels requires that larger geographic areas be served by schools that offer specialized education.

Leadership in the development of the science of agriculture has centered in the land-grant colleges and universities. Their origin was the Morrill Act of 1862 passed by Congress and signed by President Abraham Lincoln. The growth of the idea that resulted in income from federal lands being assigned to the states to establish a new type of liberal and practical education in agriculture and the mechanic arts usually is described as the work of Congressional leaders in the immediately preceding decade. Highly significant contributions had been made by Presidents Washington and Jefferson, both of whom wrote clearly and in persuasive detail that the education of persons to use land wisely for agricultural production was fundamental in the economic and political stability and progress of the nation.

During the first twenty-five years of resident education in the land-grant agricultural institutions, a growing awareness that research must be an essential function prompted Congress to pass the Hatch Act of 1887. Quite logically the next quarter century saw the emergence of demand for wider, more rapid and direct dissemination of the results of public-funded research, particularly to benefit persons who could not attend resident college courses. The Smith-Lever Act of 1914 established cooperative extension service to citizens and encouraged local participation.

The movement toward universal public elementary and secondary education accelerated prior to and shortly after World War I. Literacy shortcomings were evident in military service examinations. Requirements for skilled workers in industries and for greater agricultural output per man stimulated Congressional leaders to press for enactment of vocational education legislation. Educators who had experimented successfully with forms of occupational education in several states were consulted. The timing was right; small towns and rural areas were ready to support four year high schools and there was a young science of agriculture to teach to persons who wanted it and were able to profit from it.

Vocational Education Legislation

Three major acts of Congress have stimulated local school districts to include agricultural education in their specialized course offerings. They are the Smith-Hughes Act of 1917, the George-Barden Act of 1946 as amended, and the Vocational Education Act of 1963. The latter amends the other two and supplementary acts. For this reason the Vocational Education Act of 1963 will be given the most detailed description and explanation. Federal funds are authorized to assist states in occupational education and training as a part of several additional programs of recent social legislation that have important implications for agriculture.

The Smith-Hughes Act. Under the sponsorship of Senator Hoke Smith and Congressman Dudley Hughes, both of Georgia, the National Vocational Education Act was passed in 1917. It appropriated funds for salaries, proportionately allocated to the states on specified population bases, and requiring equal matching by the state or local community, for vocational education in agricultural subjects and in trade, industrial, and home economics subjects.

Widely quoted in interpretations to the public, often referred to in policy discussions among administrators and school board members, and regularly presented in teacher education classes have been the following excerpts from Section 10:

> That in order to receive the benefits of such appropriations for the salaries of teachers, supervisors, or directors of agricultural education such education shall be that which is under public supervision or control; that the controlling purpose of such education shall be to fit for useful employment; that such education shall be of less than college grade and be designated to meet the needs of persons over fourteen years of age who have entered upon or who are preparing to enter upon the work of the farm or the farm home; that the State or local community, or both, shall provide the necessary plant and equipment . . . ; that such schools shall provide for directed or supervised practice in agriculture . . . ; that the teachers . . . shall have at least the minimum qualifications. . . .[1]

---

[1] Public Law 347, Sixty-fourth Congress.

The offer of Federal matching funds achieved its purpose in getting many rural communities to hire teachers of agriculture and of home economics in their high schools. The decade of the 1920's was a period in which many secondary schools expanded to four-year programs and introduced departmentalization of subject areas. Curriculums in vocational agriculture, vocational home economics as well as in commercial work were established. Most schools had one teacher in each field. Students either took all of the subjects in one of the occupational curriculums or else a complete program of academic college-preparatory subjects.

It might have been anticipated that progress in agricultural science and mechanization would have resulted in increased size of individual farms and greater productivity per man in the 1930's. The great economic depression reversed the movement of workers from rural areas to cities. Teachers of agriculture were called upon to aid low-income families to obtain a living under difficult circumstances. Opportunities for employment in positions requiring higher levels of education and training were severely limited. There were good things that resulted. Many schools taught classes of young adult farmers and farm workers. Efficiency in farm business management and in marketing were stressed and important practices in soil conservation initiated.

Several supplementary acts of Congress extended the basic provisions of the Smith-Hughes Act and added appropriations. The National Defense War Training Acts between 1940 and 1944 provided funds for classes that prepared adults to contribute quickly to increased food production needs. Temporary instructors had to be hired. New patterns of supervision were devised to supplement standard teacher education procedures. Federal funds were used for the first time to rent space and to purchase equipment, particularly for agricultural mechanics and food processing instruction.

During World War II many men and women whose previous economic pattern had been that of a primarily subsistence type of farming with relatively small gross product worked in industrial plants. Need for technician education became generally recognized. Employment in office occupations, in distribution, and in many new types of services influenced the shaping of post-war vocational legislation.

The George-Barden Act.   While it may have seemed that the main objective was to authorize more money for vocational education programs, the George-Barden Act of 1946 also stimulated expansion in several specific areas. Distributive education became a training field. Salaries for state directors were authorized. Travel expenses became reimbursable. Purchase and rental of equipment were approved within a ten percent limit. Expenses of attendance at professional meetings deemed necessary were authorized. Equal matching with state and local funds was continued.

Senator Walter George, Georgia, and Congressman Graham Barden, North Carolina, sponsors of the act, used very selective criteria for allocation of funds to the states. The proportion of total allotments for agriculture was based on farm population per state, home economics funds on rural population, trade and industrial funds on urban population, and distributive education allotments on total population.

Perhaps the most noteworthy provision of the George-Barden Act, from the viewpoint of vocational agriculture, was mention for the first time of the Future Farmers of America. The wording was ". . . including supervision by the vocational agriculture teachers of the activities, related to vocational education in agriculture, of the Future Farmers of America . . ."[2]

It was by act of Congress in 1950 that the Future Farmers of America was incorporated in the District of Columbia.[3] The highly successful FFA, as a youth leadership training organization and intra-curricular occupational training aid, was thus formally complimented. The legal details involved relinquishing of the corporate status of the FFA in the State of Virginia, and acquisition of the Future Farmers of America Foundation, Inc. formed in 1944 to receive gifts from industrial and other donors and to make awards to students and former students of vocational agriculture. Trends toward broadening the scope of occupations for which education in agriculture is offered, as encouraged by recent major legislation, will be responded to by the FFA with appropriate adjustments in sponsored activities.

The Vocational Education Act of 1963. Thorough study and careful preparation by many citizens and educators went into the drafting of Public Law 88–210, the Vocational Education Act of 1963. As the Congress and the Administration were about to sponsor Federal legislation for the several levels and types of education,

---

2 Public Law No. 586, Seventy-ninth Congress.
3 Public Law No. 740, Eighty-first Congress.

President Kennedy in 1961 in a special message to Congress said:

> The National Vocational Education Acts, first enacted by Congress in 1917 and subsequently amended, have provided a program of training for industry, agriculture, and other occupational areas. The basic purpose of our vocational education effort is sound and sufficiently broad to provide a basis for meeting future needs. However, the technological changes which have occurred in all occupations call for a review and re-evaluation of these acts, with a view toward their modernization.
>
> To that end, I am requesting the Secretary of Health, Education, and Welfare to convene an advisory body drawn from the educational profession, labor, industry, and agriculture, as well as the lay public, together with representatives from the Departments of Agriculture and Labor, to be charged with the responsibility of reviewing and evaluating the current National Vocational Education Acts, and making recommendations for improving and redirecting the program.[4]

The twenty-five member Panel of Consultants on Vocational Education included five persons representing agriculture. More than a year was spent in assembling and discussing data on past and current vocational education programs. Enrollments and costs were compared. Occupational placement, mobility and other adjustments of graduates were charted. Evidences of technological change and estimates of future employment trends were provided by professional aides.

Before proceeding to write a set of recommendations for new legislation the Panel of Consultants searched for the most useful standards by which future programs of vocational education should be evaluated. Understandably, general agreement favoring a recommendation that systematic, periodic evaluation be a basic consideration in designing and implementing changes influenced the group throughout the period of its work. The value orientation was toward the individual, the aim being to make appropriate vocational education of high quality continuously accessible to citizens in all occupational categories. This differed markedly from the theme of the report of 1914 of the Commission on National Aid to Vocational Education that led to the Smith Hughes Act.[5] It had emphasized

---

[4] Quoted in Report of the Panel of Consultants on Vocational Education, *Education for a Changing World of Work* (Washington, D.C.: U.S. Government Printing Office, 1963).

[5] *Report of the Commission on National Aid to Vocational Education.* (Washington, D.C.: U.S. Government Printing Office, 1914).

the needs of industry for workers in the most common occupations, and argued that vocational education was a wise business investment and necessary to maintenance of world markets.

Section 1, the declaration of purpose, of the Vocational Education Act of 1963 is so inclusive and of such general importance to the new all-fields approach that it is presented in entirety before giving specific attention to the broad provisions for agricultural education:

> It is the purpose of this part to authorize Federal grants to States to assist them to maintain, extend, and improve existing programs of vocational education, to develop new programs of vocational education, and to provide part-time employment for youths who need the earnings from such employment to continue their vocational training on a full-time basis, so that persons of all ages in all communities of the State—those in high school, those who have completed or discontinued their formal education and are preparing to enter the labor market, those who have already entered the labor market but need to upgrade their skills or learn new ones, and those with special educational handicaps—will have ready access to vocational training or retraining which is of high quality, which is realistic in the light of actual or anticipated opportunities for gainful employment, and which is suited to their needs, interests, and ability to benefit from such training.[6]

Where funds appropriated by previous acts had been used by the states almost entirely for high school student programs and for part-time retraining and continuing vocational education of employed adults, the Vocational Education Act of 1963 requires that 33⅓ percent of each state's allotment for any year including fiscal 1968 and 25 percent for any subsequent fiscal year must be used for full-time study by persons who have completed or left high school or for construction of area vocational education school facilities, or both. Thus, post-high school technical training will become a generally available type of public education.

The establishment of new vocational education programs is not limited by any listing of occupational fields. In the definition of vocational education in the act a part of the wording, however, specifically mentions business and office occupations and the existing fields of the George-Barden Act and amendments. Vocational or technical training or retraining is given in schools or classes:

---

[6] Public Law 88–210, Eighty-eighth Congress, 1963.

> . . . conducted as part of a program designed to fit individuals
> for gainful employment as semiskilled or skilled workers or tech-
> nicians in recognized occupations (. . . but excluding any pro-
> gram . . . considered professional or requiring a baccalaureate or
> higher degree)[7]

The definition further includes vocational guidance and counseling
in connection with the training, related instruction and instruction
necessary for the student to benefit from the occupational training,
preparatory and inservice training of vocational education teachers,
teacher educators, supervisors and directors and travel of students
and vocational education personnel. The acquisition and maintenance and repair of instructional supplies, teaching aids and equipment are in the definition, but the construction or initial equipment
of buildings or the acquisition or rental of land are not, except as
separately provided under the section on construction of area vocational education school facilities.

Each of the existing vocational education fields has been broadened by an amendment to the George-Barden and Smith-Hughes
Vocational Education Acts. For agriculture the amendment states:

> . . . any amounts allotted (or apportioned) under such titles, Act,
> or Acts for agriculture may be used for vocational education in any
> occupation involving knowledge and skills in agricultural subjects,
> whether or not such occupation involves work of the farm or of the
> farm home, and such education may be provided without directed
> or supervised practice on a farm.[8]

Nearly all of the existing local high school programs in agricultural
education are organized chiefly or entirely for instruction in agricultural production (farming and ranching) and in closely related
services. The increased Federal appropriations will stimulate improvements in the quality of instruction and aid introduction of education for prospective and present farm owner-operators, technicians, and skilled and semi-skilled workers in schools that have not
had it. Directed or supervised practice, proven over the years to be
essential, may be modified and extended, but surely is to be continued.

Special provisions of the Vocational Education Act of 1963 for
research and for experimental, developmental, or pilot programs

---

[7] *Ibid.*
[8] *Ibid.*

have encouraged leaders in agricultural education to initiate studies
and programs to determine needs and opportunities in off-farm
agricultural occupations and to create and test new course materials,
teaching procedures, and evaluation devices. As commercial businesses, industries, and services as well as trade organizations and
governmental agencies write job descriptions for an increasing number of positions, evidence of demand for technical knowledge and
skills in agricultural sciences appears. The complexity of relationships makes assignment or acceptance of responsibility for training
difficult. In addition, other recent Federal-State programs provide
occupational education and training as means of accomplishing social goals.

*Other public programs of occupational education in agricul-
ture.* The land-grant colleges of agriculture are the principal
source providing teachers to guide vocational and technical education programs for agricultural occupations. They also provide
nearly all of the baccalaureate and higher degree graduates for professional positions requiring training in agricultural sciences. High
school and post-high school technical education in agriculture
serves to motivate young men and women with adequate scholastic
ability to enroll in the agricultural colleges.

Nondegree courses of agricultural study at the technician training level are offered in many but not all of the American colleges
of agriculture. Kellogg and Knapp said of them:

> The nondegree courses must have an important place somewhere
> in the system for agricultural education to meet several needs of
> both youth and agriculture. In agriculture, as in other fields a de-
> clining number of jobs are available for the untrained and unskilled.
> Some young men who lack the aptitude or motivation for the full-
> degree course can benefit enormously from training in general farm-
> ing, in one or more phases of specialized farming, or in one of
> several lines of technical training that fit them for service work
> somewhere in the broad field of agriculture.[9]

Some two year programs in colleges of agriculture failed when they
were conceived as a recruitment device for the four-year curricula.
Nondegree students have objectives, and may have aptitudes, that
differ from those of the four-year students. Several colleges grant an

---

[9] Charles E. Kellogg and David C. Knapp, *The College of Agriculture: Science
in the Public Service* (New York: McGraw-Hill Book Company, 1966), p. 130.

associate degree to students who complete two-year programs of high quality technician education. There are shorter courses in widely diversified specialized areas. Most are offered on the main campus of the university where experienced staff members, research facilities, and instructional equipment are readily available.

The colleges have exhibited tendencies toward discontinuing the nondegree programs in favor of supporting the development of post-high school courses in area vocational technical schools or in community colleges. Kellogg and Knapp offered these comments:

> Each college of agriculture has a basic responsibility to appraise continually the changing needs of agricultural education. This takes study and discussion with informed individuals and groups throughout the state. As needs arise, they can be detected, and the college can plan ways for meeting them, either with its own staff and facilities or elsewhere. The time to give help and leadership is before educational gaps become critical and people have already taken public positions on alternative plans.[10]

Preagricultural programs have been organized in some local community colleges and at branch campuses of state agricultural colleges. General education courses may serve the same function when students are given effective guidance toward transfer to a four-year college of agriculture. This is preprofessional education. If in the same institution students who desire technical education for more immediate employment are enrolled in the classes in agricultural sciences uncertainty as to the proper objectives of the instruction may result. Probably in the years just ahead as area vocational-technical schools increase in numbers, expand in specialized offerings, and attract highly qualified instructors the needs for post-high school education of technicians in agriculture will be more effectively served than by preprofessional curriculums.

The Cooperative Extension Service in each state has developed adult education programs for farmers, programs in home economics, and youth programs. A recent volume edited by Sanders,[11] had selected state agricultural and home economics extension administrators, specialists and agents, as contributing editors. They used as a heading for a large section of the volume the very appropriate and

---

[10] *Ibid.,* p. 134.
[11] H. C. Sanders, ed., *The Cooperative Extension Service* (Englewood Cliffs, N.J.: Prentice-Hall, Inc., 1966).

function-revealing term—Planning for and Effecting Change. The chapters describe activities of county agents and of regional and state specialists: visits, office calls, result demonstrations, meetings, tours, field days, clinics, workshops, news stories, exhibits, bulletins, radio and television. Persons who request and benefit from the services of a county agent in his role as adviser, teacher and organizer are referred to by the professional staff as the extension clientele. The term has merit and deserves comment (intended to stimulate further thoughtful consideration by the reader). The citizens served by agricultural extension benefit in economic and social ways. The advice and instruction are free, funds having been provided by Federal and state appropriations. There is no limit on the diversity of population groups who may and do participate.

Kellogg and Knapp reported that cooperative extension leaders, as they reflect the attitudes of the colleges, are discussing adjustments in programs and making changes that can be grouped into a few main areas:

1. Current programs in farm technology are needed that give advice in depth to commercial farmers and others according to their special needs.

2. Future extension programs will go beyond farm technology and help farm people and rural groups with social and economic problems. . . .

3. Extension will be concerned even more than now with helping rural and mixed rural and urban counties . . . with economic development and planning to make the best decisions on resource use. . . .

4. A substantial part of the extension program can be oriented toward nonfarm clientele in two ways: (1) Extension needs to concern itself with other aspects of agriculture, including agricultural service and processing industries. (2) Along with the rest of the college of agriculture, extension will contribute to solving problems of urban living. Much is being done now. . . .

5. The extension service of most colleges of agriculture will become even more closely coordinated with extension activities of other parts of the land-grant university. . . .[12]

The Cooperative Extension Service issued a publication by Phifer and Spurlock[13] describing other Federal-State educational programs

[12] Kellogg and Knapp, *op. cit.*, pp. 185–186.

[13] Bryan Phifer and Doyle Spurlock, *Federal-State Programs for Occupational Education and Training.* Federal Extension Service, United States Department of Agriculture (Washington, D.C.: U.S. Government Printing Office, 1966).

about which Extension workers and lay leaders should be informed in order to work most effectively with community planning groups and to aid eligible individuals to avail themselves of the training. The Vocational Education Act of 1963 was the first program listed.

The Manpower Development and Training Act of 1962 as amended[14] aims to relieve unemployment caused by automation, shifts in market demands, and other economic changes. Unemployed or underemployed adults who need occupational training in order to become qualified for types of jobs in which there are manpower shortages are eligible. It is the responsibility of the Department of Labor, through the offices of State Employment Services, to locate the needs for workers with specific skills. The local offices interview, test, counsel and refer prospective trainees to schools that offer appropriate vocational training. In many instances schools have organized new programs upon request, and discontinued them after the particular job openings in the area have been filled or when there are insufficient eligible trainees. There have been some classes for agricultural production workers but the most likely demands will be for technically trained workers in specialized off-farm agricultural occupations.

The joint relationship of the Department of Health, Education, and Welfare with the Department of Labor at all levels in the MDTA program shows results that can have long-range mutual benefits. Studies are being conducted by the Department of Labor on evaluation of and research in the unemployment problem, through grants or contracts. There are studies of on-the-job training and pilot projects to increase the mobility of unemployed workers. Basic education for some older people and disadvantaged young adults must precede or accompany occupational training, experience with the MDTA program in schools has shown, and is now authorized and encouraged.

The Economic Opportunity Act[15] has several sections dealing with education, especially occupational education that will contribute to employability and citizenship development of young men and young women. Some Job Corps training centers and Neighborhood Youth Corps work-training programs are directed toward the conservation of natural resources in rural areas and others utilize skill

---

14 Public Law 89–15, The Manpower Act of 1965.
15 Public Law 88–452, 1964.

training activities in urban areas. The programs try to help young people to stay in school, to return to school, and to remedy basic education deficiencies. Other acts passed by the Eighty-ninth Congress to assist states to make occupational education accessible to more persons may have significant implications for training in agriculture.[16] The National Vocational Student Loan Insurance Act authorizes funds for loan insurance programs to be administered by states and nonprofit private institutions to assist students who do not have reasonable access to financial support for attendance at trade or other technical or vocational schools. With Public Law 88–210 funds authorized for college programs of less than baccalaureate degree, the student loan sections of the Higher Education Act may be able to solve critical financial needs of students preparing for agricultural occupations. Title I of this act supports community service programs, the definition of which includes solution of problems such as housing, poverty, government, recreation, employment, youth opportunities, transportation, health, and land use. The State Technical Services Act, which may come to be known as an extension service for small businessmen, and for commerce and industry, undoubtedly will be of value to off-farm agricultural supplies businesses, to agricultural products marketing industries, and to other services in which some employees use knowledge and skills in agricultural sciences.

The Elementary and Secondary Education Act of 1965 is most comprehensive of all the Federal legislation affecting education. The act emphasizes financial assistance to low income families. To the considerable extent that these persons are in rural areas and in predominantly agricultural states, the funds will tend to up-grade general education in the schools where vocational and technical agriculture are taught. Also, many research projects and pilot programs supported by states and local school districts with funds of the act will deal at least partially with preparing young people to make a better transition from school to work. Earlier experiences in the context of current and future occupations should raise the aspirations of boys and girls interested in careers related to agriculture

---

[16] *Enactments by the 89th Congress Concerning Education and Training.* Committee on Labor and Public Welfare, United States Senate (Washington, D.C.: U.S. Government Printing Office, 1966).

above the unskilled level and motivate them to continue their technical education beyond high school.

Federal—State—Local Relationships

Traditionally education in the United States has been considered as a function of the individual states. Only recently has a majority of citizens come to believe that there can be general Federal financial support for education without serious risk of domination that might restrict state and local freedom. During recent years the bright record of achievement of the land-grant colleges and the substantial service of Smith-Hughes vocational and technical education have often been referred to in discussions favoring greater Federal —state—local cooperation.

Funds provided by Federal legislation are for specified purposes. Usually the intention is to stimulate the states to initiate new and better programs or to help disadvantaged areas improve low quality public education and educational services. Always the states and local districts are free to invest in more than minimum offerings, as they shall decide.

The Smith-Hughes Vocational Education Act explicitly required that in order to receive apportioned funds each state should establish a State Board for Vocational Education and prepare a state plan showing kinds of vocational education, schools and equipment, nature of instruction, qualifications of teachers, supervisors or directors, plans for teacher education, and plans for supervision. The Vocational Education Act of 1963 retained the requirement that a state plan be approved by the Commissioner of Education and added certain items. Periodic evaluations of programs in light of current and projected manpower needs and job opportunities shall be made. An annual report shall show that Federal funds were used to meet the occupational education needs of all groups of persons named in the act. Other new Federal education acts incorporate the basic requirement of a state plan and of an annual report on outcomes as well as expenditures.

The state plan is used in supervision of local programs. It is the source of standards that form the basis for initial approval and for annual review of the kind and quality of programs for which state reimbursement is requested. In many ways, the state plan is a set of policy statements. Some state plans, before the Vocational Education Act of 1963 was passed, had made allowance for approval by state supervisors of reimbursement for experimental programs not covered in the plan. Few local schools applied. It is probable that, with financial incentives and a growing favorable attitude of citizens toward educational experimentation, more local and area schools will submit carefully written applications for funds to conduct pilot programs.

Agricultural Education in the Local Community

Vocational and technical education in agriculture in all of the states, in communities that have provided it, has been outstandingly successful because of its relevance to the total occupational development pattern of each student. Individualized instruction and involvement of the family group in the educational growth of the student have been important. Supervised work experience, or cooperative education, on home farms of students whose occupational objective is agricultural production, has made vocational agriculture purposeful.

Leading commercial farmers, who are well educated today, serve on school boards in communities where there are substantial farming opportunities open for young men who can become established in large scale individually owned agricultural production businesses. Instruction in agriculture must contribute to (1) advancement for those who go directly from high school into farming, and who should have supplementary school-sponsored continuing adult education in agriculture and related subjects, and (2) those who need basic guidance and instruction in high school in order to enroll in post high school technician training or in professional curriculums in colleges of agriculture.

Owners and managers of businesses, industries, and services that supply inputs to commercial farmers or are engaged in agricultural products marketing also serve on school boards or contribute to educational leadership in local communities in a variety of ways. They support occupational education for farmers, and preprofessional or pretechnical education for others. In addition, both farmers and businessmen everywhere in the United States today are directing attention to adjustments in agricultural education that will equip individuals for employment in off-farm agricultural businesses, industries and services. Initial employment must be above an unskilled level, and continuing adult education is necessary for satisfactory persistence and advancement on the job.

American communities today are on the whole education oriented. Management personnel in corporate organizations are qualified and willing to share in designing school programs. Business and professional leaders, both as individuals and as members of service clubs and other community groups, have demonstrated innovative skill and desire to work with school administrators. To teachers of agriculture the content of the chapters that follow is familiar. It has been part of their professional preparation, enhanced by years of experience and by inservice teacher education. Interdependence in society and among segments of the business world is well recognized. It is just as fundamental among the general education and occupational education fields of public schools. School administrators, curriculum directors, guidance counselors, vocational and technical education supervisors and teachers in all subject fields may explore supporting education, team teaching, or other ways to make appropriate agricultural education accessible to all persons.

CHAPTER II

Objectives for Agricultural Education

A democratic society is based upon primacy of concern for the individual. The welfare of citizens is largely influenced by governmental actions taken for the dual purposes of serving the public interest and the rights and opportunities of the individual. The two objectives are worthy and proven to be compatible when applied respectively to agriculture and to agricultural producers, related workers, and consumers. Legislation to control production and prices, to provide funds for research, to conserve natural resources, or to set quality standards applies to agriculture and the public interest. Programs of agricultural education supported by Federal, state and local appropriations increase the employability of all persons who are interested, and who have personal characteristics and motivation to profit from it.

Objectives are not static; they evolve as general personal and social goals change. Scientific and technological advances including automation are powerful factors. Population changes, shifts in food preferences, national defense needs, and world markets influence persons to prepare for careers in particular fields in agriculture. Continuous appraisal of objectives and course content are required if instructional programs are to educate competent, versatile, adaptable individuals equipped to succeed in occupational fields using some proportion of knowledge and skills in agriculture.

Stages in Evolvement

To trace briefly a sequence of periods in the development of public school instruction in agriculture may aid in understanding current objectives. A few elementary and secondary schools, mostly in rural areas, taught general agriculture as a subject before 1900.

It was in the first decade of this century that serious discussion of and experimentation in vocational education in a few states created a national awareness of need for occupational training. Normal schools introduced agriculture to those students preparing to be teachers as a general biological science. Practical subjects with economic utility were added in order to get more boys and girls to continue in school and thereby acquire a better general education.

"To fit for gainful employment" was the controlling purpose of the Smith-Hughes Vocational Education Act of 1917. In the first few years state administrators were preoccupied with establishment of local programs. The teachers turned to college textbooks and bulletins for subject matter content. Supervisors paid attention to class and laboratory procedures as they strove to improve the instruction. The requirement of supervised practice resulted in wide adoption of the home project as a method for high school teaching of agriculture. Establishment of graduates in farming was the principal criterion of studies of evaluation of programs.

The influence of World War I and of scientific farming based on research at the land-grant colleges, made efficient production the aim of instruction in agriculture. As economic research increased, the measures of success shifted to effective management, and for sound reasons. During the 1920's the leaders in agricultural education concentrated upon ways and means to improve supervised farming practice as a teaching method. The home project was recognized as a boy's first experience in learning to manage a livestock or crop enterprise on a farm. Job analysis was strongly promoted. Teachers were urged to spend most of the time with students helping them learn approved practices in the productive farm enterprises predominant in the local community.

The organization of local public school vocational and technical education in agriculture within the framework of comprehensive programs intended to serve all phases of personal and social development of students has meant that good citizenship is a fundamental objective. Hamlin made his position evident by contrast in the following:

> There are two ways of viewing the public interest in agricultural education. One arises from concern about making agriculture an efficient industry. . . . The other emphasizes agricultural education as a means of developing good American citizens and good human beings. . . .
> There can be no compromise between these approaches. Education must emphasize human and social values; agriculture must be made a means of attaining these values. . . .

When a clear-cut decision of this sort has been made, new possibilities of agricultural education are opened. It may serve, not only in developing farmers and future farmers, but in the development of all of the other kinds of people in our society.[1]

Statements of purposes or objectives for vocational education have been prepared every few years by committees appointed by the Agricultural Education Division of the American Vocational Association in cooperation with the Agricultural Education Service, U.S. Office of Education. Publications listing purposes and objectives were issued in 1931, 1938, 1940, 1955, and most recently in 1966. Each time, a prefacing statement said that consideration should be given to the needs of the people for a complete program of vocational education of which agricultural education shall be an integral part. Even today few communities have achieved this goal; the Vocational Education Act of 1963 may make it possible, hopefully in a few years.

In the statements of purposes from the 1930's to 1955 seven objectives were listed, the separate publications mainly differing in supplementary descriptions. Phipps quoted from Vocational Division Monograph No. 21, U.S. Office of Education, *Educational Objectives in Vocational Agriculture,* revised 1955, as follows:

The major objectives of vocational education in agriculture for farming are to develop effective ability to:

1. Make a beginning and advance in farming.
2. Produce farm commodities efficiently.
3. Market farm products advantageously.
4. Conserve soil and other natural resources.
5. Manage a farm business effectively.
6. Maintain a favorable environment.
7. Participate in rural leadership activities.[2]

The placement function of occupational guidance was in the first ability, "To make a beginning and advance in farming." Agricultural production, marketing, and business management were the science content objectives. The conservation of soil and other natural resources goal may be traced to the establishment of the U.S.

---

[1] H. M. Hamlin, *Public School Education in Agriculture.* (Danville, Ill.: The Interstate Printers and Publishers, Inc., 1962), pp. 10–11.

[2] L. J. Phipps, *Handbook on Agricultural Education in Public Schools* (Danville, Ill.: The Interstate Printers and Publishers, Inc., 1965), p. 13.

Soil Conservation Service in 1933. "To maintain a favorable environment" was explained as the maintenance of a satisfactory level of family and community living. Social needs during the years of the great depression persuaded leaders to emphasize non-economic purposes. The leadership development objective for high school boys has been carried out through activities of the Future Farmers of America organization. Persons in post-high school young adult farmer classes in some schools have had a local Young Farmers Association for further leadership training. Ultimately the students have been aided in becoming effective members of adult agricultural and community organizations.

Because Federal interpretations of the Smith-Hughes and George-Barden Vocational Education Acts specifically limited agricultural education to preparation for farming the objectives did not mention off-farm agricultural occupations. Indirect references were made from time to time about promoting guidance and leadership opportunities in order to establish young men in organizations related to agriculture and in agencies directed toward the development of rural life. Federal reporting forms asked the states to list separately the numbers of students formerly enrolled in vocational agriculture who were placed in related positions. The subject matter they had studied, and their supervised work experience, were presumed to have been the same as for students who became established in farming.

Similarly, schools were encouraged to take credit for numbers of former students enrolled in agricultural colleges. Recognition that a particular boy might go to college caused many schools to arrange for courses that would meet academic entrance requirements in science and mathematics.

Rather than listing here the omissions and inadequacies of the traditional objectives of vocational education in agriculture, current objectives will be discussed. Attention will be given to program modifications now being tried out in schools. The changes reflect what are believed to be needed adjustments in objectives.

Current Objectives

An experiential heritage in agriculture is a cherished asset of millions of American families. Those that own and operate commercial farms normally expect each generation of sons and daughters to be educated for the responsibilities of management of the business. In addition, there are other paths to successful careers in agricultural production for persons not reared on family owned farms.

In trade center areas, both large and small, surrounded by agricultural producers, specialized businesses and services furnish inputs to farmers or function in processing and marketing. Owner-managers prefer to hire beginning workers who have had occupational experience in agriculture.

It is logical, therefore, that the first two major program objectives for vocational and technical education in agriculture as outlined in U.S. Office of Education Bulletin 1966, No. 4 should be:

1. To develop agricultural competencies needed by individuals engaged in or preparing to engage in agricultural production.
2. To develop agricultural competencies needed by individuals engaged in or preparing to engage in (off-farm) agricultural occupations other than agricultural production.[3]

The first two objectives deal with the types of gainful occupations in which knowledge and skills in agricultural science and technology are required. The third and fourth are concerned with occupational guidance and with occupational placement. Guidance involves decision-making about courses to be taken in preparation for entry into one of a cluster of related jobs. It means assisting students to obtain occupational information and exploratory experiences. Part-time employment for wages, especially in the form of cooperative education, contributes very effectively to guidance.

Occupational placement is a function that colleges perform for professional graduates. Proprietary business, trade, and technical schools attract students largely on their promise to obtain jobs for those who complete the training. Local offices of the State Employment Service annually place many seasonal, part-time workers in agricultural production and are in charge of selection and placement of underemployed adults enrolled in Manpower Development and Training programs in schools.

Area vocational and technical schools are developing contacts with employers of their students. High schools may seriously con-

---

[3] *Objectives for Vocational and Technical Education in Agriculture.* U.S. Office of Education Bulletin 1966, No. 4 (Washington, D.C.: United States Government Printing Office, 1965), p. 4.

sider accepting the placement function. Persons who enroll for continuing adult education courses in agriculture are most likely to profit not only from the additional learning but also from guidance and placement service.

The third and fourth major objectives are stated this way:

3. To develop an understanding of and appreciation for career opportunities in agriculture and the preparation needed to enter and progress in agricultural occupations.
4. To develop the ability to secure satisfactory placement and to advance in an agricultural occupation through a program of continuing education.[4]

To achieve full self-realization, the development of the individual personality to its greatest potential, requires skill in human relationships. Formal schooling should equip each learner to continue to be self-educative. Business relationships demand that each worker be an effective member of a team that includes employers, supervisors, other employees, customers, and often extends beyond the circle of economic-oriented associates.

It is appropriate that the fifth and sixth objectives be presented as a pair. Leadership is more likely to be exerted by individuals who are skilled in human relations. It is, however, different and something more. Certainly every person needs opportunities to practice leadership, and to evaluate the results of his performance. In agricultural occupations it is common that persons are self-employed or that their jobs have a combination of functions some of which call for independent decisions and the expression of leadership in organizational relations.

The last two of the major program objectives of vocational and technical education in agriculture follow:

5. To develop those abilities in human relations which are essential in agricultural occupations.
6. To develop the abilities needed to exercise and follow effective leadership in fulfilling occupational, social, and civic responsibilities.[5]

Lists of contributing objectives are given in Office of Education Bulletin 1966, No. 4, the source of the six major program objectives that have been presented here. The contributory objectives suggest course of study content and learning activities and are, conse-

---

[4] *Ibid.*, p. 5.
[5] *Ibid.*, p. 5.

quently, more related to the ways and means of teaching. Discussion of selected contributory objectives is included in later chapters.

Relation to Age and Ability Groups

The order of the wording of the statement in the Smith-Hughes Act that agricultural education shall "be designed to meet the needs of persons over fourteen years of age who have entered upon or who are preparing to enter upon the work of the farm or of the farm home" has many times been quoted to show that vocational education in agriculture should be provided first for adults. The George-Barden Act specified that funds may be used "for training and work-experience training programs for out-of-school youth."

The Vocational Education Act of 1963 permits a state to use its allotment of funds for six purposes, the first four of which name groups of people: (1) Vocational education for persons attending high school; (2) Vocational education for persons who have completed or left high school and who are available for full-time study in preparation for entering the labor market; (3) Vocational education for persons . . . who have already entered the labor market and who need training or retraining to achieve stability or advancement in employment; (4) Vocational education for persons who have academic, socio-economic, or other handicaps that prevent them from succeeding in the regular vocational education program; (5) Construction of area vocational education school facilities; (6) Ancillary services and activities to assure quality in all vocational education programs, . . .[6]

High school students and adults.   The Report of the Panel of Consultants on Vocational Education[7] stated that while vocational agriculture enrolled more adults in evening classes than high school students in full-time programs, ninety per cent of teacher time and Federal funds had been spent on high school classes. Similar proportions held true for trade and industrial programs. These comparisons influenced the new legislation. One third of the funds, and after fiscal 1967–1968 one fourth, shall be used only for purposes (2) or (5) or both.

The few states that have had long experience with full-time post-

---

6 Public Law 88–210, *op. cit.*
7 *Education for a Changing World of Work, op. cit.*

high school technician education in agriculture, such as Massachusetts, New York, and California, are being asked to give advice on curriculum construction and to prepare course of study guides. New programs are started in junior colleges or area vocational technical schools in states including Washington, Oregon, Colorado, Minnesota, Illinois, and North Carolina.

High schools in rural areas plan to continue to offer full-time high school instruction in agriculture. They have excellent opportunities to expand their services with classes, both of high school students and adults, in off-farm agricultural occupations that will need more workers with technician level knowledge and skills. The quality of instruction for young adult commercial farmers needs continuously to be raised. To do the adult instruction that communities should have will mean hiring a second or third instructor.

Students with special needs.   There have been few formal programs of vocational education in agriculture for disadvantaged or handicapped youth or adults. Studies, and pilot programs, have considered the special problems of low income farmers. Teachers have provided individualized instruction for high school boys of low ability and for some with other handicaps, but this has been done in regular classes in agricultural production.

The Manpower Development and Training Act, the Economic Opportunity Act, and parts of other Federal education programs will serve needs of socio-economic and culturally disadvantaged persons in the immediate future. Training and other allowances are important features. The role of teachers of agriculture may be that of assisting in situations where those teachers have special competence.

Relation to Occupational Levels and Groups

Commercial farmers, as self-employed businessmen, often have been described as needing to have managerial ability as well as scientific knowledge, mechanical competence, and experience in semi-skilled operations. A young man may progress from farm laborer to a skilled equipment operator, to technician, and to owner-manager. In the past, teachers of agriculture organized the units of instruction on an enterprise basis, e.g. beef production, field corn growing, etc. Enrolled youths or adults ranged from farm hand to manager in occupational objectives. Technological advance and specialization may demand a differentiation by occupational levels.

Occupational levels. In 1964–1965 surveys of off-farm agricultural occupations in twenty-six states showed that several hundred job titles in the major product and service fields could be classified broadly into inclusive occupational levels, such as:

1. Managerial
2. Professional
3. Technical
4. Sales
5. Clerical
6. Service[8]

Managers, many of whom maintain medium-sized or small businesses and services also are the owners. They must have the highest degree of competence in nearly all of the agricultural product knowledge areas pertinent to the business, in economics and business management, and in human relationships. If a business employs professional workers, a college degree level education is likely a minimum qualification.

In some businesses involved with farmers needs or that process and market agricultural products, technical level employees serve as fieldmen or are in charge of quality control. Where giving advice or solving problems calling for decisions based on scientific or economic knowledge is frequent, a fieldman probably is a professionally educated person. Technicians are defined as employees serving as aids to professionals. One or two years of full-time education in applied science describes the preparation of technicians. Cooperative education is a highly regarded training method.

Salesmen are more like managers than service workers in off-farm agricultural businesses. They must have product information, human relations skills, and highest competence in marketing and distribution. Clerical workers need office and business training and in businesses where they deal directly with farmers and other customers should know production management and practices related to products handled and services performed.

---

[8] *Summary of Research Findings in Off-Farm Agricultural Occupations* (Columbus, Ohio: The Center for Research and Leadership Development in Vocational and Technical Education, 1965).

Service workers are classified by many different job descriptions including skilled mechanic and supervisor, processor, equipment operator, and others. Training and related work experience are essential. Advancement depends upon continuing education while employed. A distinction should be made. Education for advancement *in* an occupation for which there is a fairly precise job description may be the objective of supplementary courses for homogeneous groups of employed persons. Preparatory education classes enroll people whose objective is initial employment or change to a new position.

Influence on Programs and Courses

That appropriate education in agriculture shall be an integral part of the total development of individuals who as workers or as citizens want it and can benefit from it is the aim of programs and courses. Specifically, immediate objectives of teaching-learning experiences for particular students vary with age and maturity, with ability and aspiration, and with employment status. Estimates of prospects for the future in each occupational area influence the establishment of new programs and the modification or discontinuation of present programs.

Agriculture is more than farming. Persons engaged in commercial agricultural production know that their lives are committed to a basic industry. The challenges to produce high quality products, to be efficient, to conserve and use resources wisely, to promote family welfare, and to contribute to society are powerful and worthy motivations. Education along those lines is essential and it must be accessible. Individual objectives for each student must be desirable, immediate, specific, and attainable.

Vocational and technical education in agriculture for the millions of workers in off-farm agricultural occupations is expanding rapidly. Cooperation with other vocational fields will make combinations of courses available to students. Each vocational field can provide supporting education, from small to large amounts, for students majoring in other fields. Complex occupational requirements of positions in many businesses demand flexibility and adaptability.

Agriculture is a combination of basic and applied biological sciences and economics. Mechanization of operations has made the physical sciences and engineering increasingly important. Management level personnel in agriculture must know how and when to hire specialists, and this takes breadth in their own education.

Objectives of agricultural education will continue to evolve. New groups and neglected groups of people will be served by imaginatively created programs. Schools may decide that they can afford to teach agriculture in elementary grades and as general education in secondary schools without Federal vocational funds. Women may enroll in special courses both in preparation for wage earning and for consumer interests or appreciation values. Emerging objectives need not long await implementation if citizens clearly state their aims and vigorously discuss them.

CHAPTER III

Curriculum and Courses of Study

Curriculum components in agriculture are a part of a school vocational and technical education. In many ways the relationship is similar to that of vocational education to the total general education program in a secondary school. Structuring of content to be taught has been influenced by the organization of basic and applied departments or disciplines in the colleges of agriculture in land-grant universities. The basic natural sciences are reorganized only gradually, as illustrated by the change of bacteriology to microbiology. The reorganization of fields of agricultural technology has been much greater in the last few years. Directions for further desirable changes may not yet be clearly apparent. Divisions of plant science and animal science in colleges have replaced separate majors for students by types of crop and livestock. Divisions or curriculums in food technology and in agricultural resources are examples of current reorganization.

Education for professional employment in agriculture is occupational education. It is not difficult for schools offering agricultural education of less than baccalaureate level to reorganize their courses to meet current and potential needs of students whose employment will be in other-than-professional positions. In contrast, the elementary and secondary school curriculum reform projects in mathematics, the sciences, social studies, and English have been conducted by persons in the academic disciplines. In appraising assets and limitations of curriculum changes, Goodlad observed that:

> Reaction in current curriculum reform against supposed overemphasis in previous decades on problems of social living and self-adjustment has resulted in heavy emphasis on problems inherent in the disciplines. . . . Planning from the top down and within the structures of the disciplines has tended to slight the developmental processes of learners—their interests, the irregularity of their growth, and their individual differences. . . . The need to clarify educational objectives for purposes of selecting what to teach and

28

evaluating both pupil performance and program effectiveness is a first principle, one that is increasingly being reinforced.[1]

The high school student who elects to study agriculture is an individual, a youth growing toward young adulthood. He is a member of a family group, in which he has learned to accept responsibilities. As a student in a school in a community, he has earned a place in a societal unit more impersonal than the family, but in which small groups organize for widely diversified functions. Such a group is composed of those whose participation in common activities is in vocational and technical education for agricultural occupations.

Subjects and courses of study are the content of the curriculum along with all of the planned learning experiences for students, whether or not directly related to subjects taught. In high school, a student who elects agriculture has added a specific curriculum element, the effect of which on his general educational development may be considerable. Post-high school and adult programs differ in sequence of courses, in proportion of technical and general content, and in the immediate goals of the curriculum.

Curriculum Components

The objectives of vocational and technical education in agriculture listed in Chapter II have guided, but only partially determined, the curriculum for full-time students. Constraints of time, school size and organization, qualifications of teachers, financial resources, adequacy of physical facilities, and perhaps above all, the inflexibility and inertia of established institutions are factors that delay change. Curriculum components related to the six objectives, presented as three pairs, will be discussed in reverse order from their presentation, thereby moving from the general to the specific elements. In doing so, all of the subjects and services of the school are included.

General education, human relations and citizenship. As never before, the American people are committed to education for all. In the elementary grades language arts and communications skills precede the alternative sequences of English courses in high school.

---

1 John I. Goodlad, ed., *The Changing American School.* Sixty-fifth Yearbook of the National Society for the Study of Education, Part II (Chicago: The University of Chicago Press, 1966), pp. 48–51.

Speaking, writing, reading, listening, comprehending all contribute to the ability to think rationally and to act responsibly. Mathematics, science, and social studies are the other major subject areas. In most secondary schools it is usual for students to complete sequences of courses in each area. Barlow, in developing the rationale for vocational education, treated the relation with basic liberal education this way:

> The vocational educator's concept of the total education required for each individual is not particularly different in theory from that of the "Liberalist." It is deplorable to find a high school graduate, or even a dropout, who cannot read, write, speak, or calculate with facility. It is similarly deplorable if he does not have a thorough understanding of the American way of life or of his cultural heritage. It is further deporable if he cannot find employment because he has not prepared to enter the world of work.[2]

Modern mathematics courses to be taken in high school by students electing agriculture who have scholastic aptitude sufficient for success in college (and it is right to assume that they will go) should be determined by each student's interests and ability. Further differentiation in mathematics may be possible in large schools along lines of preparation for specializations in biological sciences, physical science and engineering, or economics and businesses that will be studied later in professional or technical programs.

It is psychologically sound, and it is efficient, for agriculture instructors to teach the applied mathematics required in their courses. Quality control in many steps in the processing and distribution of agricultural supplies and products involves sample measurements and calculations. Decision-making is a management function requiring the mathematics of input-output relationships. Accounting procedures are used to some degree by nearly all persons in agriculture.

By the time students reach senior high school they have had a sequence of general science courses in junior high school grades. Some schools offer biology or earth science as separate courses as early as seventh, eighth, or ninth grade. More and more attention is being directed toward science teaching in elementary grades. In-

---

[2] Melvin L. Barlow, ed., *Vocational Education.* Sixty-fourth Yearbook of the National Society for the Study of Education, Part I (Chicago: The University of Chicago Press, 1965), p. 4.

ductive reasoning, discovery, and experimentation with environmental phenomena enrich the opportunities for individual student growth. Senior high schools offer electives in chemistry, physics, earth and space science and biology. Biology organized with an ecological approach and chemistry emphasizing food industry processes, quality tests, and consumer understanding are recommended.

A teacher of agriculture is a professional as much because he comprehends and values basic science principles beyond the level of an agricultural technician as that he is skilled in learning theory beyond the level of a curriculum materials aid. Vocational education uses specific knowledge and skill training as both ends and means; ends in that students are equipped for entry into a position that exists today, and means in terms of dynamic participating experiences that encourage students to learn science principles.

Citizenship education is the purpose of the social studies in a school curriculum. History, political science, sociology and economics may be separate courses or taught in combinations. To transmit the cultural heritage to the next generation is a traditional objective of education as a function of the state. How well it is accomplished depends upon the administrative disposition of funds and time, the qualifications of teachers, the attitudes and support of the community, and the individual capacity of each student to learn.

Leadership and cooperative activities of the Future Farmers of America, the organization of high school students studying vocational agriculture, also contribute to citizenship development. For instance, community service projects bring students into contact with the needs of society and they provide opportunities for boys to observe citizenship attitudes and the performance of influential adults. Principles of economics may be learned from supervised work experience, which for farm-reared students centers in the ownership and management of commercial-scale production enterprises. There are possibilities for improvement in economics education through the joint efforts of agriculture teachers with instructors in social studies and business subjects.

The major curriculum areas of secondary schools other than those that are occupation oriented have been described. State departments of education in specific instances are charged by state laws to require local schools to include special subjects in particular grades and for minimum numbers of hours. Health, physical education, art, music, industrial arts, and driver education are examples. They are less than full one-credit courses and have to be classified under general education.

Concept of the Individualized Curriculum

Before outlining in detail the courses of study and major instructional units in agricultural education, one of the curriculum areas with an occupational objective, a question is worth raising about whether a school has curriculums or each student pursues an individualized program that in total becomes for him a curriculum. Does the degree of freedom in choosing combinations and sequences of subjects make this possible? Is it the function of educational guidance to assist each student to construct an individually tailor-made curriculum? How important is a degree of commitment to a more or less definite occupational goal in the selection of a pattern of courses?

To raise these questions at all implies that more than a single rigidly prescribed group of subjects may prepare students to move successfully toward the same long-range goal. This is a good thing, especially in view of changing and emerging interests that may motivate the student. Integration in the final analysis always is achieved by the student. The totality of school experiences, under wise guidance, should at every stage in the student's development contribute in a balanced manner to the exercise of his full potential. Supervised farming experience, or cooperative education through employment in an off-farm agricultural occupation, while enrolled in courses in agriculture is individualized instruction.

Instruction Areas in Agriculture

Major instructional areas in vocational and technical education in agriculture are organized on the basis of groups of occupations requiring competence in specialized agricultural science subject matter fields. They are (1) agricultural production (farming and ranching), (2) agricultural supplies, (3) agricultural mechanics (sales and service), (4) agricultural products (processing and marketing), (5) ornamental horticulture, (6) forestry, (7) agricultural resources, and (8) other agriculture.[3] Each area may be a separate curriculum. Agricultural production has been the single program offered in rural high schools under the provisions of the Smith-Hughes and George-Barden Vocational Education Acts. The other areas have been taught in technical institutes or junior colleges in a few states.

The broadened definition of agriculture in the Vocational Education Act of 1963 has encouraged many high schools and area vocational-technical schools to make employment surveys and to act to establish programs in one or more fields in addition to or other than vocational education for commercial farming. Studies in twenty-six states, mostly completed in 1964–1965, show that agricultural supplies, agricultural products (processing and marketing), and ornamental horticulture are the off-farm businesses and services that will employ the largest numbers of workers needing knowledge and skills in agriculture in the next five years.[4]

Agricultural production. From 1917 to 1964 the term "vocational agriculture" was used to describe rural high school programs for establishment and advancement in farming. There were no other major instruction areas or curriculums. The course content varied with the crop and livestock enterprises of communities, regions or states. Classes were organized for high school students in grades nine through twelve. There were continuing education classes for out-of-high school young farmers and for older adult farmers. Now known as agricultural production, these types of classes will continue to serve the largest total numbers of students.

Agricultural production may be defined as an organization of subject matter and learning activities concerned with principles and practices in the production of livestock, field crops, fruits and vegetables, fiber and other crops, on commercial and part-time farms. In addition to animal science, plant science, farm mechanics, and farm business management, instruction specific to each production enterprise is emphasized. Knowledge and skills taught involve the eco-

[3] An adaptation of a classification by an Office of Education *ad hoc* committee of persons in agricultural education and industries at a meeting in Washington, D.C., February, 1966. *See also:* Glenn Z. Stevens, "Instruction Areas in Agriculture," *Agricultural Education Magazine* XXXIX, No. 5 (November, 1966), 104–105, 110.

[4] *Summary of Research Findings in Off-Farm Agricultural Occupations.* The Center for Research and Leadership Development in Vocational and Technical Education (Columbus, Ohio: The Ohio State University, 1965).

nomic use of agricultural land, labor, capital and management. The efficient operation of modern farm equipment and the harvesting and marketing of high quality products are important functions that require skill and technical knowledge. Examples of occupations in agricultural production are general farmer, livestock farmer or rancher, dairy farmer, fruit grower, farm manager, and farm equipment operator.

The dairy cattle, beef cattle, swine, sheep and poultry enterprises employ a very large proportion of agricultural production workers, predominantly self employed owner-operators who use knowledge and skills in animal science. Meat animals, dairy products, poultry, and eggs accounted for 66.3 per cent of net farm sales of food products that totalled over twenty-six billion dollars in 1964.[5] Animal science principles and practices in nutrition, genetics, physiology, animal health, production management, marketing and related areas are instructional units in the curriculum.

The production of field and forage crops, tree fruit and nut crops, small fruit crops, vegetable crops, farm forestry products, and other crops together employ the agricultural production workers who use knowledge and skills in plant science. Fruits and vegetables, grains for food, oil-bearing crops, and other food products made up 33.7 per cent, nearly nine billion dollars, of net farm sales of food products in 1964.[6] Important plant science instructional units in an agricultural production curriculum are soils, plant nutrition, plant genetics, plant physiology, pest control, production management, marketing and related areas. Most producers of meat animals and dairy products grow grain and forage crops that are fed to beef cattle, swine, sheep and dairy cattle on the farm and, therefore, have need for technical knowledge and skills in plant science.

For several reasons farm mechanics is treated as a separate element in the agricultural production curriculum. It deals with physical science knowledge and skills. Modern farms must have a large investment in power and equipment, structures, and automation devices to achieve competitive labor efficiency. Instruction in the selection, safe operation, maintenance, and repair of machinery and

---

[5] *Food from Farmer to Consumer*. Report of the National Commission on Food Marketing (Washington, D.C.: United States Government Printing Office, 1966), p. 7.
[6] *Ibid.*

equipment contributes substantially to lowered costs of production. The schools teach farm mechanics in a well-equipped laboratory, called the agricultural mechanics shop. It is feasible to teach this phase of agricultural production at the school using tractors, farm machinery and other equipment from the home farms of students, or loaned by dealers, to provide learning experiences that duplicate the abilities needed from day to day in a farm service center. These relate to farm power and machinery, farm structures and conveniences, farm electrification, the mechanics of soil and water management, and other farm construction and maintenance. Skills and knowledge are needed in internal combustion engines, power transmission, maintenance mechanics, welding, concrete construction, uses of electricity, materials handling, systems development and other applications of mechanics in agriculture.

Farm business management is basically decision making. It involves the manipulation of production inputs to achieve chosen goals in terms of output volume, quality and efficiency. The units of instruction are farm accounts, performance records, budgeting and analysis, purchasing, marketing, financial and legal management, farm organizations, government programs and other applications of economics and business practices. This phase of agricultural education is most appropriate for adult farm owner-operators and farm managers. Careful selection of course content will introduce high school students to management principles and operations.

Agricultural supplies.   Businesses that furnish production needs to farmers deal in specializations and combinations of manufacturing, sales, and services. The principal physical supplies purchased by farmers are agricultural chemicals, livestock feeds, farm crop seeds, crop fertilizers, petroleum and other supplies including small equipment. Usually the business that handles supplies for farmers also will furnish services such as grinding, mixing, conditioning and application. Examples of occupational titles in agricultural supplies, in which workers need knowledge and skills taught by schools in courses in agriculture, are (1) agricultural supplies manager, (2) agricultural chemicals fieldman, (3) seed salesman, (4) fertilizer applicator, (5) agricultural supplies installation and service mechanic, and (6) feed mill equipment operator.

An agricultural supplies business may be a local, individually or family owned enterprise. Many today are units of state-wide, regional or national corporations. Farmers purchasing cooperatives have similar status, and needs for technically educated employees. Course content for students employed in or preparing to enter the agricultural supplies field should combine agricultural education with business education. Managers, fieldmen, and salesmen who deal directly with farmers, particularly those who give consulting service, need considerable knowledge of animal science, plant science, and agricultural business management.

Competency ratings by employers interviewed in state surveys show high need for general business skills, salesmanship, and employee relations by managers and salesmen, and medium need by service workers.[7] An understanding of agricultural chemistry, nutrition, animal health or pest control, and business management marks the difference between technician level employees and most service workers. Courses of study in agricultural supplies, sometimes labeled agribusiness, have been developed to the highest degree of specialization in non-degree programs in community colleges and area vocational technical schools. Increased differentiation in this direction is planned in high school agriculture departments. Students will be given participating work experience by cooperative arrangements with nearby businesses. School faculties will create patterns of supporting education among occupational departments.

Agricultural mechanics (sales and service). This area of instruction is important enough to be a curriculum specialization in area vocational schools, technical institutes and community colleges whose graduates are needed in farm machinery dealerships in regions of high farm production. It deals with sales and service of agricultural power units, mostly tractors, integrated machinery, and related equipment. Agricultural mechanics will be concerned with agricultural food products processing and marketing equipment in a greater degree in the future. Examples of job titles are (1) agricultural mechanics service manager, (2) agricultural machinery salesman, (3) agricultural mechanics partsman, and (4) agricultural machinery mechanic.

Some positions in each of the fields of agriculture, both on-farm and off-farm, require knowledge and skill in mechanics. As a curriculum area, then, agricultural mechanics sales and service should

---

[7] Reference is to individual state publications abstracted in *Summary of Research Findings in Off-Farm Agricultural Occupations, op. cit.*

be organized to provide short unit courses to students whose occupational objectives are in, for instance, ornamental horticulture, agricultural supplies or agricultural resources. Taken one step further in the integration of all fields of vocational education, highly competent agricultural mechanics instructors may teach courses for some students in distributive education or selected trades and industries. Conversely, students who hope to be agricultural machinery managers can profit by electing business courses and those aspiring to advance as highly skilled mechanics should take trade and industrial unit courses.

Agricultural products (processing and marketing). After farmers have produced quality products, the modern American food industry is organized to perform many services and operations including assembling, sorting, testing, grading, processing, manufacturing, storing and marketing. Some of the functions maintain the quality of the product; other operations add value. The numbers of employees in off-farm agricultural products processing and marketing businesses who need knowledge and skills customarily taught in food technology courses in colleges and technical schools vary with the product and with the responsibilities assigned to job titles in the business. The numbers are large at the points closest to direct dealing with producers. After finished products reach the supermarket, or other retail trade outlet relatively few employees need agricultural education for greatest service to their organizations.

The major food product areas in an agricultural products processing and marketing curriculum are (1) meat, poultry, and eggs, (2) dairy products, (3) fruits and vegetables, and (4) grains for food. Examples of food marketing occupations in which technician level knowledge and skills in agriculture are used are meat processing manager, fruit and vegetable market manager, livestock buyer, dairy processing equipment operator, grain elevator operator, agricultural commodity grader, and quality control technician. Major non-food agricultural products are cotton, tobacco and wool.

Courses in the curriculum include the physical and chemical properties of foods, composition and ingredients of processed foods, formulations and additives. The methods of preservation as related to quality and consumer preference influence the actual practices of canning, pasteurizing, freezing and other operations. Quality control instruction includes not only proficiency in making tests but also requires knowledge of regulations and should give the learner an understanding of the microbiological and other changes that must be controlled. For some employees business abilities are very important, for others special training in mechanics is of value. Adult education for present employees, by increasing their worth to the business, may also aid in raising the job entry qualifications and wages.

Ornamental horticulture.   Three types of businesses and services that produce, distribute, and utilize horticultural plants for ornamental values are floriculture, nursery management, and landscaping and turf establishment and management. Greenhouse production and sales, nursery production and sales, garden center sales and services, landscaping, groundskeeping, greenskeeping and arboriculture are occupational as well as business areas. Some courses in ornamental horticulture will serve several or all of the occupational areas but others have to be specific to the type of product or service. Examples of ornamental horticulture job titles are florist, greenhouse manager, nursery grower, garden center salesman, landscape aid, greensworker and tree pruner.

School greenhouses are used to teach skills in flower growing and nursery propagation. Floral design and arrangement classes are interesting to girls. There have been programs, perhaps, with an imbalance of use of instructional time. More hours than needed have been devoted to routine greenhouse practices and not enough to instruction in horticultural principles and in efficient business management. A justification could be that some students are slow learners or otherwise in need of a non-demanding experience. Individual needs may be served, but not truly occupational goals.

Many persons are hired on a seasonal basis to work in each of these areas of ornamental horticulture. Such jobs are desirable for youths but provide insufficient employment for adults. Owners and managers of nurseries and garden centers are diversifying their businesses to find productive work for year-round employees during slack seasons. Another difficulty that education can help remedy is the situation wherein many unskilled persons are hired at low wages to do hand work. More efficient labor management, greater use of mechanization, an improvement in quality of products, and increased returns therefrom, should result from technical education in this field.

Forestry. The central function of technical education in forestry is to prepare workers for the management of trees grown as a crop. Other aspects of employment at less than the professional level are in forest protection, logging, wood utilization, special products production, and cooperation with persons whose work is in conservation or recreation. Some occupational titles in forestry for which technical education is appropriate are forestry aid, Christmas tree grower, sawmill operator, logger, and log scaler.

The colleges regularly have graduated an adequate supply of professional foresters. Some increase in two-year programs at the associate level is taking place. There are virtually no other educational programs in forestry, yet more than half the land in many states is in forests. High school vocational agriculture has made no more than a beginning in teaching the management of farm woodlands. The curriculum content for vocational and technical education in forestry includes forest management, forest protection, logging, wood utilization, special products, recreation, and other courses in regional demand.

Agricultural resources. As a curriculum, agricultural resources is an organization of subject matter and learning activities designed to provide opportunities for students to study principles and processes in the conservation and improvement of environmental resources such as forested and other natural areas, fish and wildlife, soil, water, and air, and with the establishment, management, and operation of outdoor recreational facilities. Examples of agricultural resources occupations in which vocational and technical education in agriculture may be used are (1) recreation farm manager, (2) soil conservation aid, (3) wildlife conservation officer, (4) fish hatchery worker, (5) game farm worker, and (6) park worker.

The course content and supervised practice activities appropriate to preparation for entry or advancement in occupations in conservation, recreational utilization, and services connected with agriculturally related natural resources is structured to treat the multiple uses of forested and other natural areas, wildlife management,—including game farms and hunting areas, and fish management,—including fish farms and hatcheries. Conservation and utilization of soil, water, air and other resources are taught in the context of regional planning for public, industrial and home owner benefits. A knowledge of legal aspects is important. Many employment opportunities are in government and have regulatory functions to be performed. Many students majoring in other occupational fields will profit by at least one course in resource management.

Other agriculture. No formal curriculum has been prepared or proposed for high school students whose occupational objective is to prepare for a professional position in agricultural fields in industry, government, education or other services. If one of the previously outlined curriculums is closely related to the higher education goal of the student, he should enroll for selected courses in it while scheduling adequate college preparatory required courses. The same advice should be given the student who plans to complete a two-year associate degree or technical school program in a field of agricultural technology. This is consonant with the introductory discussion in this chapter suggesting that adequate guidance will help each student to have an individualized curriculum.

Before students, teachers, parents, and advisors uncritically accept a recommendation that all students planning to enroll in agricultural colleges should take only academic subjects in high school, the preparatory values of some high school experience in agriculture should be appraised. First, the programs must be of high quality; that should be the situation generally. Next, the school schedule should provide the needed English, mathematics, science, and social studies with sections suited to the ability level of the student. This leaves room in a normal student load for a course in agriculture, one each year if the student is interested and sees relevance for his future.

The community oriented learning experiences of a well-taught course in agriculture broaden the acquaintance of the student with organizational leadership patterns and give him the practical life experience a college student is assumed to have had. Also, in professional programs that would like students to have had previous farm experience, high school agricultural education is a replacement for having been reared on a commercial farm. Most small schools will be able to offer only one to three curriculums or majors in agriculture. Students whose occupational goal is in a miscellaneous, non-professional area may elect courses and combinations most likely to contribute to entry level competence.

Course of Study Patterns of Organization

Schools and colleges teach some courses organized on a production enterprise basis, such as swine production, turkey growing, broiler production, potato production, or pasture management. Other courses organized on a science principles basis carry titles as animal nutrition, plant physiology, plant genetics, soils, or milk secretion. Perhaps courses on irrigation, soil conservation, weed control, farm buildings, or livestock marketing are somewhere on a continuum between production enterprises and science principles.

The terms "functional experience unit" and "problem solving approach" often are used to describe agriculture courses organized on a farm enterprise basis, especially when the students engage in growing the crop or producing the animal product as a supervised occupational experience part of the course. In contrast, a "subject matter unit" and a set of "lessons" refer to a subject-matter-to-be-learned teaching procedure in which the content significance for the individual may not be immediate or goal-oriented.

Teaching-learning activities that encourage individual initiative, discovery, creativity, and that value individual estimates, appraisals or decisions are more likely to characterize the instructional relationship in which the teacher is a guide or catalyst rather than a classroom authority, an assigner of tasks. Inductive reasoning is a component of purposeful learning. Careful examination of laboratory teaching will help guard against over use of deductive exercises for the sake of practice or proving the point. Reinforcement is a versatile and stimulating concept, repetition has less significance in occupational education.

Agricultural education for farming gradually developed an almost total commitment to courses of study based on the enterprises of the local community and, carried one step farther, on the home farm business. Population mobility, increased occupational specialization, and competition of valuable general education courses for the student's time have motivated sweeping reappraisals. Time is an important factor in learning. Quite likely there is psychological importance in the association of a student with a teacher of agriculture who gets to know the student well over a sequential period of more than one year and who is concerned with the total development of the individual. This does not say that each student must take all of the unit courses in agriculture. Nor is there proof that small bits of learning must be taught seasonally. Modifications of the cross-section or horizontal pattern of course of study construction must be given trial. Teaching efficiency probably can be improved by new patterns of course of study organization.

CHAPTER IV

Teaching High School Students

Vocational education in agriculture is presently an elective area in the high school curriculum. It enrolls students for whom agricultural education of high quality "is suited to their needs, interests, and ability to benefit from such training."[1] The Vocational Education Act of 1963 further states that vocational education "is given in schools or classes (including field or laboratory work incidental to) . . . , and is conducted as part of a program designed to fit individuals for gainful employment as semiskilled or skilled workers or technicians in recognized occupations. . . ."[2] The interpretation is that each student shall have a recognized occupational goal. To prepare to enter and advance in farming is, very broadly conceived, an occupational goal. Any one of many specific job titles may be an immediate, or intermediate, objective. The curriculum may be designated as agricultural production. Within it some courses or units provide students with the technical knowledge and skills currently required for entry into specific employment categories.

In that agriculture is elective, and occupationally based, it differs from English, mathematics, science, or social studies. Particularly it is unlike English,—a subject generally required in all grades of a high school, in which the enrollment of students and placement in sections of courses is more a matter decided by each student's past achievement than by future purposes in life. Selection of students for advanced mathematics and science may be a screening process with only high ability students admitted. This process is applied to enrollment in some technical education fields, such as chemical technology and electronics technology. High school enrollment in agriculture, to date, has been principally a decision of the student with information and guidance assistance of teachers, parents, and friends. As school counselors become better acquainted with the changes in agricultural technology, the content of new courses

---

[1] Public Law No. 88–210, Eighty-ninth Congress, 1963.
[2] *Ibid.*

taught by better prepared teachers, and the expanded opportunities for employment in agricultural occupations requiring more education, they will better serve many students with rural backgrounds— and urban students, too, with interests in agriculture.

Student Enrollment and Orientation

To be reared on a farm or to visit relatives or friends engaged in off-farm agricultural occupations are excellent ways to develop interests in this important segment of the economy. Early years in school may provide learning experiences of significant import. Science, economics, distribution, service, communications are being emphasized in elementary schools, with the instruction carefully chosen to be at the maturity level of the child. In discussing groups unserved by agricultural education, Hamlin directed attention to possibilities for better education in junior high schools:

> Agriculture has been taught largely in the smaller communities in which junior high schools have not been common, but as school districts increase in size, more junior high schools are being established in school systems in which there are teachers of agriculture. Agricultural education in the junior high schools is providing many boys and girls with orientation to agriculture, information about opportunities and requirements in the agricultural occupations, knowledge they need in their present and prospective agricultural activities, a realistic and meaningful approach to the sciences, particularly biological science, and an interest in pursuing further the study of agriculture.
>
> In the senior high school there are many students who have and will continue to have agricultural connections of some kind, who do not wish to enroll for three or four years of vocational agriculture. A high percentage of those who become farmers or engage in other types of agricultural work do not know, as late as the senior year in high school, that they are to engage in this type of work. There are represented in the senior high schools students who will inherit farm land and agricultural businesses, engage in agricultural professions after college, marry men employed in agriculture, and have other agricultural relationships. Their education should not be destitute of agricultural education. The rank-and-file of senior high school students need at least to know the agricultural relationships of the natural sciences and the social studies.[3]

[3] Hamlin, *Public School Education in Agriculture, op. cit.,* p. 105.

The program of the junior high school must be challenging and rewarding for many students to persist in school to high school graduation. It should arouse in students, most necessarily in the disadvantaged, a compelling desire to succeed, to earn a diploma, and with it to be prepared for employment or advanced education. Byram introduced the concept of pre-high school orientation to agriculture this way:

> The success of students in school has an important bearing on their choice of and preparation for a career, and on their educational plans, including how long they will stay in school. . . . The responsibility for assisting youth with problems met as they enter high school and take part in its educational activities is jointly shared by the teacher of agriculture with the rest of the school staff and with parents. . . . In a true community school . . . in which agriculture has been a part of the curriculum for a long time and has been well interpreted to the people, and in which pupils go to school in the same or adjoining physical plant to the one housing the high school, the pupil in his last year of elementary school or junior high school will be quite well informed about high school and the program of agricultural education. Teachers generally, however, should not assume that this understanding is sufficient.[4]

Because teachers of agriculture regularly instruct individual high school students and adults on home farms and in agricultural business establishments where supervised practice is being carried out as an integral part of a course in agriculture, they become personally acquainted with many junior high school students and have opportunities to answer questions about high school, including possible enrollment in agriculture. A planned visit to the home of each junior high school student who may elect agriculture is a systematic part of the program in many good schools. The time for the visit is in the spring months while the student is in the grade preceding the first year that vocational agriculture is taught in the high school. Parents ask about courses, objectives, cocurricular activities, supervised occupational experience, and post-high school education. In turn, student and parents furnish valuable information to the teachers about interests, aspirations, and capabilities.

Group techniques of pre-enrollment orientation have advantages.

---

[4] H. M. Byram, *Guidance in Agricultural Education,* (Danville, Ill.: The Interstate Printers and Publishers, Inc., 1966), p. 130.

Phipps listed worthwhile outcomes and illustrated activities often used:

> Some problems of choice and adjustment may be profitably handled in groups rather than through individual counseling. For some problems, group techniques are even superior to individual counseling. Group techniques may save the time of an instructor. They may aid students to recognize, define and verbalize their problems. In some instances individuals are more willing to discuss and think through problems of choice and adjustment with their peers than with a teacher or counselor. . . .
>
> Some teachers assist in orienting pupils to high school by visiting elementary schools. . . . Many high schools have visiting days for prospective pupils. . . . FFA chapters invite prospective pupils to visit certain FFA meetings and events. . . . A chapter may also provide a program for the local 4-H clubs as a means of helping the younger members of these clubs to learn more about agricultural education and the high school.[5]

A group technique of pre-enrollment guidance that high schools where agriculture is taught are finding to be very useful is the administration of the Vocational Agriculture Interest Inventory. Excerpts from the manual for the instrument explain the purposes, procedures, and interpretations:

> The Vocational Agriculture Interest Inventory is to be used by guidance counselors and teachers of agriculture in high schools to assist eighth grade students in deciding whether to elect vocational agriculture. All eighth grade boys should take the test. Those with high interest scores can be identified and counseled prior to selection of ninth grade courses. . . . The inventory may be administered to ninth grade students if vocational agriculture in the school is offered first in the tenth grade. . . . When high schools were small, teachers of agriculture had an opportunity to counsel with all students who desired to elect vocational agriculture. The complex task of assisting large numbers of students to make course selections is no longer the sole responsibility of one teacher. . . .
>
> The scores of eighth grade students in the research project revealed that high scores [or middle scores] were predictive of success in ninth grade vocational agriculture. . . . Many students with high or middle scores will elect agriculture with no counsel. Others will have to receive adequate counseling to disclose their interest to them and to their parents. . . . In general, if a student with a low score desires to elect agriculture, the guidance counselors and teach-

---

[5] L. J. Phipps, *Handbook on Agricultural Education in Public Schools, op. cit.,* pp. 585–586.

ers of agriculture should discuss his interest inventory score with him and try to determine whether he has a valid reason for electing the course.[6]

The research reported in the manual included administration of the Kuder Preference Record—Occupational, Form D, to the same one thousand boys in twenty high schools. Keys for both inventories were developed on the items in which the criterion group, students who one year later were "Successful Vo-Ag Students," differed significantly from the norm group, all "Other Students." The manual reported that individual students who had high scores on the Vocational Agriculture Interest Inventory tended to have high scores on the Kuder Vo-Ag Key developed in this study and on the published Kuder Farmer Key.[7] Additional research in progress indicates that the Kuder E General Interest Survey prepared for junior high school students yields scores on its Outdoor Scale that correlate with scores on the Vocational Agriculture Interest Inventory. Schools that regularly use either of the Kuder tests[8] do not need to use the Vocational Agriculture Interest Inventory, although to do so would add to the acceptance of the accumulated data.

A feature of the suggestions in the manual for the Vocational Agriculture Interest Inventory that deserves special mention is a set of forms, with actual student information filled in, showing how electronic data processing equipment may increase the efficiency of reporting and summarization, and of interpretation of relationships with other test scores, ratings and characteristics.

Guidance Activities of Teachers

Occupational development is a continuous process in the life and education of each student; educational and occupational guidance are continuous in the relationship of teachers of agriculture with students. As explained in the previous section, much is known about each student in agriculture before high school classes begin in the

---

[6] R. W. Walker, G. Z. Stevens, and N. K. Hoover, *Vocational Agriculture Interest Inventory Manual* (Danville, Ill.: The Interstate Printers and Publishers, Inc., 1965), pp. 1–8.

[7] *Ibid.*, pp. 13–14.

[8] G. Frederick Kuder, *Kuder Preference Record—Occupational, Form D,* and *Kuder E General Interest Survey* (Chicago: Science Research Associates, 1957, 1963).

fall. Likewise, new students and their parents are acquainted with the teachers, know about important choices the student faces, and have confidence that the welfare of the student is the concern of a competent, dedicated faculty and administration.

In the sections of this chapter that follow, where teaching-learning involvements with high school students are differentiated into individual instruction, class instruction, and the Future Farmers of America (cocurricular activities to develop leadership, citizenship, and cooperation), the objectives of guidance will be inextricably interwoven. Just as an understanding of basic science principles is less likely to be achieved by students if the teacher's plan does not have each principle explicitly stated as a desired outcome, a somewhat formally structured statement of objectives and activities in guidance is needed by vocational and technical education instructors.

The following outline is a modification of a longer list by Byram titled *Suggested Guidance Activities of Teachers of Agriculture*[9]

1. Student information service
   a. Obtain and record information regarding each student, his home background, previous experiences in farming and other agricultural work, and opportunities for supervised occupational education.
   b. Observe and record significant behavior of students in class and out-of-class situations.
2. Educational and occupational information service
   a. Assemble information on agricultural occupations from printed materials, visual and auditory materials, and from local and regional surveys that may involve students or a department advisory committee.
   b. Acquaint students with occupational information and educational requirements in agriculture through teaching, field trips, interviews arranged for students, and other procedures.
3. Counseling service
   a. Assist students to formulate occupational and educational goals and to broaden their experiences through actual participation in farming activities and part-time employment or exploratory contacts in off-farm agricultural occupations.
   b. Refer students to qualified persons or agencies for occupational and educational information.
4. Placement and follow-up service

---

[9] Adapted from Byram, *Guidance in Agricultural Education, op. cit.,* pp. 28–31.

    a. Regularly obtain and record information regarding local and regional occupational placement opportunities in farming and in off-farm agricultural occupations.

    b. Provide information about individual students and former students to prospective employers and assist students to be placed and to advance in suitable employment.

    c. Maintain an up-to-date placement and continuing education record of each student.

5. Cooperation with entire school staff

    a. Work with guidance counselors, supervisors and teachers in other occupational education fields to develop integrated instruction and guidance services.

    b. Assist the total effort in orienting students to the high school, cooperating with parents, citizen groups, organizations, agencies and employers, and in helping students to adjust to post-high school education and employment.

6. Evaluation of guidance activities

    a. Make evaluations through follow-up visits, conferences and surveys with students and employers.

    b. Utilize evaluation procedures applied to the total school guidance program.

Occupational information and product knowledge are different. The first applies to facts that are directly related to employment; the latter is a manufacturing, processing, sales and distribution term. There are many situations in the teaching of courses in agricultural science and practice when occupational information and guidance may be incorporated efficiently and effectively. Schools may arrange that beginning students are taught formal units on guidance before encountering the what, how, and why of product knowledge courses.

To a boy entering ninth grade, and enrolling in a class in agriculture, graduation may seem like a long-range goal. He needs to learn how to act in the school environment. Earning honors in the FFA that require three or more years to attain may motivate the boy to appreciate educational guidance. Instruction that outlines to students the alternatives in individual programs of supervised farm practice or cooperative off-farm agricultural employment experience is educational guidance, but certainly introduces much occupational information. The sections of this chapter that follow, while treating individual instruction, class instruction, and Future Farmers of America activities of high school students, recognize that much of what is done is prevocational or general to the time when the student discovers himself in the purposeful situation of deciding to enter a specific occupation.

Individual Instruction

Occupational education for employment in agricultural production has the tremendous advantage that many individual high school students live on family owned commercial farms. A background of interesting and satisfying experiences influences a student's decision to enroll in a high school vocational education program in agriculture. Parental approval generally means that the family expects to help the student advance toward ultimate establishment in farming. As the student studies agriculture and grows in understanding and skill, the family and the farm business benefit at the same time. The procedure that makes this relationship possible is known as individual on-farm instruction. Teachers of agriculture make regular visits to the homes of students who live on farms to supervise planned programs of agricultural experience.

In the last few years increasing numbers of high school students who do not live on farms have elected to study agriculture. For most of them a realistic occupational goal is employment in an off-farm business or service where knowledge and skill in agriculture are needed. Procedures have been developed to provide planned individual programs of cooperative occupational experience through employment in an off-farm agricultural business. Often the work is on a part-time basis and may be done during some of the hours of the school day. When the occupational experience is obtained on a farm other than that operated by the student's parents, the employment arrangements may be quite similar to a home farming program or it may be patterned after the wage employee experience in off-farm businesses. The "cooperative" feature means that the employer is thoroughly aware that he has agreed to instruct the student, and plans to do it in a cooperative involvement with the teachers of agriculture and the school.

Work experience and cooperative education differentiated. Before presenting the functions of teachers and the activities of students in individual agricultural experience programs, the difference between work experience as a part of general education and cooperative education which serves occupational goals should be explained. Mason and Haines make the distinction in the following five basic types of school programs using the world of work as an educational experience:

A. For general education purposes
1. *Work observation programs.* Student observes work, does not perform tasks except to understand them. Unpaid. Usually a few weeks in length at most. May be tied in with a class in which occupational information is discussed.
2. *General work experience programs.* Student performs tasks of actual job. May or may not be paid. Typically engaged in for general education values, excluding exploratory. Usually one semester or less. Limited school supervision; usually no related class.
B. For occupational education purposes
1. *Work-study programs.* Student performs in approved job situation. Usually paid and given credit. In-school instruction usually before work period and seldom tied in directly with job experiences. Typically one semester or more.
2. *Internships.* The term used for college student work-study programs.
3. *Cooperative education programs.* Occupational goals based on student's career objective. The work situation is an occupational laboratory for the classroom instruction. Selected training stations. Correlated instruction in school. Pay and credit. Consistent school supervision. Typically at least one year.[10]

Mason and Haines, teacher educators in the office and business and the distributive occupations fields, take the comparison between work experience for general education and cooperative vocational education further by stating that the latter is concerned with developing the outcomes which every worker needs to know for employability and the knowledges, abilities and attitudes which only the worker in a given occupational field needs to know. They summarize that the two methods should be recognized for that which each can do most effectively and efficiently.[11]

Cooperative education in agriculture. Teachers of agriculture have, over the past fifty years, developed highly effective procedures for cooperative education in situations where the farmer-parent is the "employer" in the instructional relationship. Now, recognizing

---

[10] R. E. Mason and P. G. Haines, *Cooperative Occupational Education* (Danville, Ill.: The Interstate Printers and Publishers, Inc., 1965), pp. 48–49.
[11] *Ibid.*, pp. 59–60.

great technological change and supported by the broadened provisions of the Vocational Education Act of 1963, agricultural education is in a period of major adjustment. Mason and Haines discussed the possibilities in combination programs among vocational
fields:

> Vocational educators have been carefully studying possible new
> roles for education in agriculture. Research and investigation have
> revealed that, in addition to farming, there are many other occupa-
> tions in which agricultural competencies are required. Such occu-
> pations may be classified broadly into two categories: (1) non-farm
> agricultural occupations in which the agricultural competencies are
> of primary importance and other competencies are of secondary
> importance and (2) non-agricultural occupations in which some
> agricultural competencies are requisite. Much research is needed
> to distinguish the two in order that the proper combinations of in-
> structional activities may be devised.[12]

In several states that in 1965 reported occupations surveys in
agriculture,[13] analyses of competencies needed by persons to enter
and to advance in recognized jobs have brought out many instances
in which supporting education in office and business, distributive,
or trade and industrial education is important. The scope and degree
of specific abilities needed vary greatly. New patterns of individual
instruction, as well as of courses scheduled, should be devised and
tested. Teachers of agriculture may broaden their own abilities, request assistance from instructors in the other fields, or make certain
that the employer teaches the student during his cooperative education experience.

The role of the agriculture department in a local or area high
school as a source of supporting education for students majoring in
other occupational fields has only begun to be identified. There are
great possibilities. Students who major in office and business education in rural high schools are hired as clerical workers in agricultural
supplies businesses: those that handle livestock feeds, crop seeds,
fertilizers and agricultural chemicals where they need selected
knowledge in animal science, plant science, and agricultural business management. Major oil companies are selling spray materials
and fertilizers at service stations. Schools are being asked to teach
appropriate agricultural product knowledge to present and prospec-

---

[12] *Ibid.*, pp. 109–112.
[13] *Summary of Research Findings in Off-Farm Agriculture, op. cit.*, pp. 15–21.

tive service station employees. In food processing and distribution, some workers use agricultural knowledge and skills. Ways must be found to use teachers of agriculture in supporting education roles for students whose individual experience programs are coordinated and supervised by instructors in other fields of vocational education. Area vocational-technical schools with large faculties and ten to twenty or more different occupational fields probably will be in the best position to develop combination programs including agriculture. If area schools offer post-high school vocational education entirely or predominantly, the needs of high school students must continue to be met in comprehensive secondary schools.

In a number of states, high school teachers of agriculture have made a start. Their experiences have been written into manuals of recommended practices. An Ohio State University publication that brought together the experiences of pilot programs and the results of national survey discussed certain basic considerations:

> Not only the school administrator but the entire school staff should understand and appreciate the values to be derived from cooperative occupational experience and recognize that the program also benefits employers as they share in the educational growth of the students.[14]

The duties and responsibilities of teachers in charge of individual students enrolled for cooperative education in off-farm agriculture include: constructing a list of general objectives and specific lists of abilities students preparing for each occupation should develop, obtaining administrative and community approval of essential policies, becoming acquainted with educational resources of the area, making business contacts and educating employers for their part in the process, counseling and enrolling students, teaching at the place of employment, teaching related units in the classroom, helping students keep records of their experiences, developing student ability to appraise progress, assisting graduates to obtain favorable employment, and making long-range modifications in the total program. Subject matter competence is important in teaching, but this job requires much more.

---

[14] *Planning and Conducting Cooperative Occupational Experience in Off-Farm Agriculture.* The Center for Research and Leadership Development in Vocational and Technical Education (Columbus, Ohio: The Ohio State University, 1965), pp. 4–6.

Individual education for agricultural production occupations.
A successful commercial farmer who had been a high school student
in vocational agriculture when asked to name the most significant
phase of his high school experience in agriculture is virtually certain
to say that it was his individual supervised farming program. To
operate a crop or livestock farm is to be engaged in the business of
agricultural production. A high school boy who lives on a full-time
or part-time farm, or who obtains employment on a farm, is in the
environment of a learning laboratory. Desire to make a beginning
in farming and to advance toward establishment in a successful
farm business is basic motivation. Teachers of agriculture and parents provide the essential guidance and technical education.

The results of *learning by doing* in agricultural education have
led to a general recommendation that the course of study in agriculture be based on a cross-section of the knowledge and skills required by the production enterprises and related activities in the
supervised farming programs of the students in a particular class.
If the supervised home farm experience program of each student
represents the best possible learning activities to contribute to a
planned, realistic, and worthy occupational objective then such
course of study planning is satisfactory. The major livestock and
crop enterprises of present commercial farmers in the community
usually offer greatest promise for students preparing to farm. On
the basis of this reasoning, teachers have built courses of study on
a cross-section of the agriculture of the community. Let us check
again the occupational goal of the student. If his goal is not the
same as the major type of farming in the community, the student
will necessarily have to obtain a larger part of his education in agriculture through individual instruction—in an appropriately planned
supervised farming program.

The components of planned agricultural production experience
must be defined. Success in agricultural production (farming or
ranching) requires business management ability. It involves knowledge and skill in livestock and crop production and marketing. The
selection, operation, and maintenance of machinery and equipment
require management, technical knowledge and skill. The conservation and wise use of soil, water and other natural resources are essential. All of these components are based on the economics of
production; they contribute to learning how to earn an adequate

farm income. In addition, individual farming activities bring the student into situations where skill in human relationships and leadership may be developed.

The object of individual instruction in agriculture, made purposeful and meaningful by the student's investment in real-life undertakings that involve risk and promise of profit, is the development of the student. Planned experiences of a ninth grade boy in his first class in agriculture must be suited to his physical and mental maturity. In succeeding years progressively expanded activities help the student to advance toward adulthood, at his own rate. Superior guidance and instruction will help him to achieve his full potential in general education development and in occupational competence.

A farm reared boy may have fed and cared for calves or other farm animals before reaching high school age. He may have assisted in crop production practices and learned to operate some of the simpler, non-hazardous farm machinery and equipment. He may have been a member of an agricultural 4-H club supervised by local volunteer adult leaders or had junior projects in seventh and eighth grade groups advised by the high school teachers of agriculture. Through youth activities like these, or just through the help and encouragement of the farm family, a student entering a beginning high school class in agriculture may actually have ownership of animals, crops, or equipment. It is capital productively invested. At the other end of the scale of experiential background are the beginning students who have had little or no opportunity at all to participate in farming activities.

A standard pattern of individual farming program planning, proven successful with many thousands of rural high school students, may be outlined as follows: (1) a small start in a major livestock or crop production enterprise is made the first year, and increased each succeeding year by means of natural livestock increase or by reinvestment of earnings; (2) a wise selection of an additional enterprise each year broadens the scope of the student's program as justified by his advance in knowledge, skill and maturity; (3) acceptance of responsibility by the student for essential conservation, mechanization, automation, construction, record keeping, or reorganization activities on the farm (often called improvement projects); and (4) achievement of a status involving an equity in the entire home farm family business (partnership arrangement or corporation membership). For only a few high school students does this degree of progress toward establishment in farming become a legal reality before graduation. It is most important, psychologically, that a young farmer advance to the level of participation in the decision-making responsibilities of an owner-manager status in his early post-high school years.

When a beginning student in agriculture selects his first livestock or crop enterprise by answering the questions of *what* and *how much,* he has made management decisions. As the student learns *how* to produce, he acquires knowledge and skill in approved farming practices—the technology of agriculture. When a student comes to understand *why* particular decisions are made and practices adopted means that agricultural science principles have been learned.

In a textbook written for the orientation of high school students as they are introduced to the planning of individual supervised farming programs Hammonds and Binkley say to the farm boy:

> You want to become independent within a few years. Independence is something that one achieves; it is achieved gradually, not all at once. A farming program offers an excellent way to achieve independence. It gives you a chance to earn some money, to make some decisions and carry them out, and to prove to parents and others that you are able and willing to assume some responsibility.
>
> If one is to farm, he must get started in farming; he must have . . . foundation animals, considerable machinery and equipment, and have control of several thousand dollars in money before he can begin farming for himself. He may or may not own some land; he may farm as a partner or he may rent a farm. Unless one inherits or is given some of these things, he must secure them by his own efforts. . . . Young men most likely to farm are those who have better than average supervised farming programs and who have sizeable investments in farming when they finish high school.[15]

Hammonds and Binkley continue to address the beginning high school student by raising the alternative, "What if you do not farm?"[16] Their advice is to consider the life-long usefulness of abilities to care for gardens, flowers, shrubbery and lawns and to make repairs and improvements around the home that were learned

---

[15] Carsie Hammonds and Harold Binkley, *Farming Programs for Students in Vocational Agriculture* (Danville, Ill.: The Interstate Printers and Publishers, Inc., 1961), pp. 33–38.

[16] *Ibid.,* pp. 38–39.

through supervised agricultural practice. Some persons will have two jobs, one of which is part-time farming on an efficient, income producing basis. The discussion is concluded with mention that employers of persons who deal with farm people prefer workers who have demonstrated proficiency in farming because such knowledge is of great value in their work.

The initial involvement of a teacher of agriculture with a student about to plan a supervised farming program takes place before or near the start of the school year. The discussion includes the parents. If the student is to obtain the experience at a location other than the home farm, the prospective employer also should participate in the conference. The personal characteristics, interests, and goals of the boy should be explored. Resources available for the student to use must be realistically appraised. They include land for crop production, housing for livestock, machinery and equipment, working capital in the form of feed, supplies, and credit available to the student. There should be a need for the boy as a worker in the total farm business. Above all, it is the job of the teacher to explain that the relationship is educational, it is a method of teaching, the outcomes are to be appraised in terms of the occupational and general education growth of the student. The boy and his family or employer must know that the teacher will come to the farm as often as needed during each year to instruct the student and to help the parents or employer do their part in the cooperative education program sponsored by the school.

Written agreements are essential. Each party should know precisely what is to be contributed. Class instruction time is used by the teacher to help the student to prepare each item in the agreement. A form of negotiation takes place with the parents; modifications and readjustments may be necessary from time to time. Making budgets, setting production goals, determining approved practices the student must learn and carry out, arranging favorable marketing, keeping accurate records, and evaluation of outcomes are steps in the learning process. Phipps expressed concern that some teachers of agriculture in the past may have thought of records as just a requirement of the state office. He feared that record keeping often has not been properly stressed; objectives for keeping records have not been developed; and little emphasis has been placed on student motivation. Since a goal of high school instruction is to have students learn to keep the records they will *use* as adult farmers, Phipps would like to have teachers understand the reasons for good records.[17]

Individual instruction of high school students in agriculture has been presented as cooperative occupational education basic to curriculums and courses. Many of the most effective classroom teaching procedures are based on the actual problem solving situations in the current experience program activities of students in the class. Challenges of greater specialization in agricultural production as well as in off-farm businesses and services will demand intensified individual instruction and larger schools that offer more courses.

Class Instruction

Class teaching in agriculture is characterized by a variety of procedures and instructional media. Contact hours with the students in a class are regularly scheduled in the agriculture science and management classroom and in the agricultural mechanics shop or laboratory. Conference-type sessions with class committee groups frequently are organized around common interests. Class field trips to farms, businesses, and industries in the community, when properly planned and executed, are very effective in class teaching. To add to a brief overview of the pattern of class instruction in agriculture, frequently used procedures include demonstrations, exhibits, assistance of invited resource persons from the agricultural industries, conduct of class or group production projects in livestock or crop enterprises and improvement projects in conservation, beautification, or other community service. Laboratory examination and testing of samples of crop and livestock products, soils, agricultural chemicals, and of machinery and equipment make high school agriculture teaching directly applicable to specific occupational preparation.

The course of study for a class that meets the equivalent of five times per week during a nine month school year is organized to include six to perhaps twelve functional experience units. A unit may be an agricultural production enterprise, such as growing field corn, managing a dairy herd, or alfalfa production. Each crop production

---

[17] See Phipps, *Handbook on Agricultural Education in Public Schools, op. cit.,* p. 264.

unit has problem areas concerned with (1) selecting the enterprise, locating a market, and arranging necessary financing, (2) allocating land and labor, selecting seed or plants, obtaining fertilizer and other production supplies, (3) using approved cultural practices, (4) protecting against insects, diseases and weeds, (5) harvesting, storing, preparing for market, and (6) keeping essential records, evaluating outcomes, and planning future changes. The outline for animal enterprises is similar: (1) selecting the enterprise, locating a market, and arranging necessary financing, (2) allocating housing and labor, selecting breeding or feeder stock, obtaining feed and other production supplies, (3) using approved production practices, (4) maintaining herd or flock health, (5) preparing products for market, and (6) keeping essential records, evaluating outcomes, and planning future changes.

Limitations of class teaching time make it necessary that only the specific crop and livestock enterprises of importance in the likely future employment of the students are taught in detail. A major unit thus becomes the context in which basic principles of agricultural science and technology may be learned. An alternative is to teach, for example, a plant science course in which the units are soil management, production practices, plant breeding, plant nutrition, plant protection (pathology and entomology), quality control and marketing. In this type of organization of subject matter content the applications of principles are selected to provide the largest possible numbers of students with educational experiences that may be called marketable skills in terms of current employment needs.

In off-farm agricultural businesses, manufacturing and processing are the "production" phase of the total enterprise. Feeds, fertilizers, pesticides, machinery and equipment are manufactured for use by farmers as supplies (inputs) in their production of food and other agricultural products. Meat, milk, poultry and eggs, fruits, vegetables, grain and oil-bearing crops, and other farm products (outputs) are processed by businesses in which some, often many but seldom all, employees need agricultural knowledge and skills. Sales and distribution functions of certain employees are more important than the agricultural competencies they should have. Services that require specialized technical education support the primary operations in agriculture. Examples are accounting and management services, custom application of materials, custom harvesting, breeding services, testing services, and aid to professional persons. Course units to teach product knowledge and skills may also develop understanding of applied science principles. Units on how businesses are organized and financed, economics, management, human relations, salesmanship, and other business procedures are appropriate for many students preparing for careers in off-farm agricultural occupations.

In the concept of a unit as a module is the idea that an organized, functionally interrelated set of learning experiences needed by students in more than one curriculum area may be incorporated into as many different courses as required. If all students should be taught the unit or module, it may well be considered to be general education and placed in a course taken by all students. General units on economics and human relations are taught in social studies courses; when taught in an occupational course, such as horticulture or agricultural mechanics, the objectives and content should be specific to the occupations and individualized for the students in the class.

Teachers of agriculture have influenced the quality of instruction in rural high schools in a very positive, constructive manner. This has not been due to chance circumstances or only to natural advantages inherent in the subject matter. It has been the result of skillfully organized learning experiences based on an understanding of principles of successful teaching. An instructor can continue self improvement by applying to the development of teaching plans for new units the same awareness of the elements in the learning process that he has found productive with his students. These elements include (1) an identification and definition of the problem situation or felt need and the purposeful selection of specific goals, (2) the formulation of a plan of action, often from a thorough search for and choice of approved practices, (3) the execution of the plan through guidance of student performance in their individual experience programs, and (4) periodic self-evaluation of results by employment of appropriate measurement devices provided by modern research in agricultural science. In brief, the phases in the psychological sequence of a complete learning experience are purposing, planning, execution and evaluation.

Purposes are established as concepts to be understood, decisions to be made, or abilities to be developed through real-life undertakings by students. Meaningful learning takes place in settings that exemplify the concepts involved whether by individuals, the class or only by observation. There are values in interaction in social situations,—a group carrying through common undertakings in which each learner has a responsible share and benefits from self-generated discipline. Not to be underestimated are the individual achievements that both stem from and contribute to the class effort. Lines of emerging meaning develop sequentially and sum to long term continuous growth. Discriminating evaluation promotes independent competence of the learner and builds confidence in moving forward to more complex undertakings.

Class instruction in agricultural mechanics frequently employs teacher demonstrations of skills to be learned. The standard sequence of teaching-learning procedures begins with an explanation of the usefulness to the students of the skill to be learned. Materials required are exhibited and named. Processes and principles are described. The actual teacher demonstration is given with accompanying comments and appropriate repetitions and answering of questions. Students practice the skill under conditions similar to those used by the instructor and with teacher supervision. A testing step in the learning process may or may not mean that the teacher observes while each student performs the skill but usually concludes with the teacher grading the quality of product by each student. Ideally there should be follow-up instruction as the student uses the skill in an actual occupational setting where it is needed. The steps just outlined are efficient in skill teaching. They do not require that the individual student have more than temporary interest or that the skill shall contribute to achievement of a complex, purposeful, personal goal.

Subject matter units in a mechanics course might be groups of skills with related information in electricity, gasoline engines or concrete, for example. Each unit would be taught simply by presenting the skills as laboratory lessons in a logical succession. The teacher's responsibility would end with the practice periods in the school shop. This is as well as can be done, sometimes, and does have a degree of prevocational value. Much better teaching, and truly vocational instruction, should result from functional experience units on the organization of a central electric power distribution system for a farm or other business establishment, the selection, operation and maintenance of tractors on a farm or of small engines used in ornamental horticulture businesses, or concrete construction of a milk house or other agricultural building.

Problem solving experiences are more than computational exercises when the decisions arrived at are actually to be carried out on a home farm or in the business where the student is employed in a cooperative occupational education relationship. The purposeful real-life problem situation of one student in a class may have significant value for other students encouraged by a skillful teacher to recognize the needs, share in assembling facts, and choose a plan of action. From this point on, the learning available is that which results from appraisal of the particular plan that was carried out by the owner-operator of the enterprise.

A land laboratory, a greenhouse, a nursery, or other agricultural production facility may be utilized for class instruction. It may be financed by the school or by the students as members of the Future Farmers of America organization with adult supervision of the teachers of agriculture. There are many ways that the FFA contributes to both individual and class instruction in agriculture while maintaining an intra-curricular status as a voluntary student leadership development activity in the high school.

The Future Farmers of America

The Future Farmers of America is the national organization of, by, and for students and former students of vocational agriculture in public schools qualifying for Federal reimbursement under the National Vocational Education Acts. The states, territories, and other subdivisions of the United States have associations chartered by the national organization. The basic unit in a school is the local chapter of FFA. Local chapters are chartered by and affiliated with an association through which the purposes, rules, and program of activities of the national organization are adopted and supported.

The objects and purposes of the FFA, as revised, include the following:

1. To develop character, train for useful citizenship, and foster patriotism, and thereby to develop competent, aggressive rural and agricultural leadership.
2. To create and nurture a love of country life by encouraging mem-

bers to improve the home and its surroundings, to develop organized recreational activities, and to create more interest in the intelligent choice of farming and other agricultural occupations.

3. To encourage the practice of thrift.

4. To strengthen the confidence of students of vocational agriculture in themselves and their work, to encourage such members in the development of individual farming programs or other supervised agricultural experience and to promote their permanent establishment in agricultural occupations by (a) encouraging improvement in scholarship, (b) providing awards to deserving students who have achieved distinction in vocational agriculture on a local, state or national level, and (c) assisting deserving students financially, through loans or grants, in becoming satisfactorily established in agricultural occupations.

5. To cooperate with others, including state boards for vocational education, in accomplishing the above purposes, and to engage in other activities, consistent with the foregoing purposes, determined by the governing body (National Board of Directors) to be for the best interests of the organization.[18]

The primary aim of the Future Farmers of America is the development of agricultural leadership, cooperation, and citizenship. The local FFA chapter in a public school is an organization *of* students enrolled in vocational education courses in agriculture. An annual program of activities is planned and carried out *by* the students themselves with adult counsel and guidance. The school provides teacher time, facilities, funds and other essential support *for* the FFA as an intra-curricular part of the total personal development of a group of its students.

The FFA appeals to motives of young people moving through adolescent years toward adulthood. The opportunity to identify with others whose occupational goals are in the broad areas of the agricultural industry is exemplified in the national blue jacket worn by members. The corn gold emblem on the jacket, on banners, and used on printed materials is made up of five symbols, described in the Official Manual as follows:

The owl is symbolic of wisdom and knowledge; the plow is the symbol of labor and tillage of the soil; the rising sun is emblematic of progress and the new day that will dawn when all farmers are trained and have learned to cooperate; the cross section of an ear of corn represents common agricultural interests since corn is na-

---

[18] *Future Farmers of America Official Manual* (Alexandria, Virginia: Future Farmers Supply Service, 1965), p. 19, as revised at the 1966 national convention.

tive to America and grown in every State; and the eagle is indicative of the national scope of the organization.[19]

To win medals, trophies, prizes and other awards may seem to adults to have only extrinsic value but to young men in the Future Farmers of America an honor earned through striving for excellence in a worthy activity is at the time highly meaningful. Often an achievement stimulates the setting of new goals and motivates further study and practice. Public speaking contests and demonstrations of parliamentary procedure in the conduct of a business meeting have developed in many boys a practical, serviceable level of communications competence. More than four hundred major business organizations throughout the country annually contribute approximately two hundred thousand dollars to the National FFA Foundation to be used for an extensive system of awards, national, state, and local, that recognize achievements of individual students in agricultural production and in related endeavors.

Group dynamics techniques need to be understood by teachers who serve as advisors to local chapters of Future Farmers of America. Each member must learn to perform in a variety of roles. The formal ritual of FFA degree ceremonies provides a framework for systematic advancement from year to year. To serve on a committee, to be the chairman of a committee, and to be elected as an officer represent stages in leadership development. Planned programs of officer training for specific duties have been found to be effective in teaching and often are scheduled on a district basis involving several schools at one time. State and national student officers are particularly inspirational when invited to serve as resource persons. Community leaders in business and professions enjoy being asked to assist in leadership training sessions and have a lasting influence on the students. They recognize that the student organization is providing experience that will be of great value to each youth a few years later when he joins adult agricultural organizations and other community service groups.

Capable leaders and interested members must have a carefully planned annual program of work and a calendar of activities. Major subdivisions of the written program of work of a local FFA chapter generally include the following headings: supervised farming or

---

[19] *Ibid.*, p. 10.

other occupational experience, cooperation, community service, leadership, earnings and savings, conduct of meetings, scholarship, recreation, public relations, and participation in state and national activities. In summarizing detailed suggestions for constructing the program of work, Bender, Clark and Taylor offered this advice:

> The best way to develop a program of work in which all members will be interested is to appoint committees to select the activities, goals, and ways and means. The goals and ways and means should be carefully selected so they meet the needs of the members, the school, and the community. Goals should be challenging yet not beyond the reach of the chapter. The recommendations of each committee should be voted upon by the members and approved by the superintendent of the school.[20]

The committees that planned the activities should be given the responsibility for supervising their execution and for the evaluation of the results. Counsel of the teachers of agriculture will assure the contribution of each project or event to the educational objectives of the course and of the school.

There are student organizations in the other fields of vocational education. Home economics students may belong to local chapters of the Future Homemakers of America. Distributive education sponsors DECA,—Distributive Education Clubs of America. In some high schools students enrolled in office and business education have local units of Future Business Leaders of America. The newest effort to promote a student leadership organization is in the field of trade and industrial education where the term VICA stands for the Vocational Industrial Clubs of America. While not representing a vocational education curriculum, the Future Teachers of America certainly is an occupationally oriented student organization. Since its members must earn a college degree before they are employable, the high school activities may be classified as preprofessional. Future Scientists, Future Librarians, Future Nurses,—in fact, any use of the word "Future" in the name of a student organization implies a common occupational goal and indicates a willingness to be guided by capable teachers in directions that add a vital element to class instruction. Students enrolled in agriculture may be confident that the Future Farmers of America is worthy of their best efforts.

---

[20] R. E. Bender, R. M. Clark, R. E. Taylor, *The FFA and You* (Danville, Ill.: The Interstate Printers and Publishers, Inc., 1962), p. 71.

CHAPTER V

Continuing Education of Adults

A complete program of education in a community is determined by the needs of all of its people at a period in time and it should be flexible in providing for the dynamic nature of the many interacting social processes. It is important in the total influence upon the future of the community that a complete program of education be recognized as that combination of desirable formal and informal educative experiences which will best promote the welfare of the individual in his family and societal functions continuously throughout life. It is believed that formal general education ought to be provided until the individual can continue to be self-educative in the broad areas of purposeful living. It has been fortunate that farm-reared boys and other rural non-farm students could begin their vocational education for agricultural occupations in the real setting of their future life work while still in high school. But, this is only a beginning; the crucial years lie ahead.

The controlling objective in long-time planning of young adult vocational education programs in agriculture is the continuous individual progress made toward becoming established in an agricultural occupation and in successful family and community living. The high school phase is a desirable preliminary period. It is difficult to find a community in which the teachers of agriculture are doing outstanding work in advising and instructing young adult farmers and other persons employed in off-farm agricultural occupations where there is anything less than a superior high school student program in agriculture. Frequent involvement in the current problems and needs of employed young adults provides teachers the very best preparation for organizing appropriate learning activities for high school students. The example of systematic instructional contacts by their instructors with adults in agricultural occupations over a period of years after completion of high school encourages younger students to approach occupational development planning with vision, confidence, and persistence.

Adult Vocational-Technical Programs in Agriculture

During the years between the two World Wars teachers of agriculture in high schools in the United States were encouraged by their state supervisors to organize and instruct separate class groups of young farmers and others of adult farmers. The "young farmers" were defined as boys between the ages of sixteen and twenty-five who might or might not have been graduated from high school and whose occupational objective was to become established in farming. The groups taught were in part-time classes. This designation originated from the practice of scheduling classes during afternoon hours in winter months when young farm laborers and sons of farm owners were not needed for field work. Most of what was taught was concerned with the rapidly developing scientific and technical knowledge in livestock and crop production available for dissemination from the state agricultural colleges. Some of the instruction dealt with remedial aspects of general education. Gradually the emphasis moved to leadership training and to the social and civic educational needs of the young men enrolled. Assistance in placement in jobs on farms and help with advancement in occupational status were highly significant to individual students.

The term "farmers evening class" was used during the two decades from 1920 to 1940 to describe a series of meetings for farmers. These were usually arranged for by a teacher of agriculture in a rural high school. It was assumed that the men who attended had achieved satisfactory establishment in farming as owners, tenants, or managers and needed only to be brought up to date on new farming practices in order to make minor adjustments in their businesses. The men who attended were likely to be between thirty and fifty years of age. The meetings usually were scheduled at night at the high school once a week for ten to twelve weeks. In school districts that covered large areas, the meetings might be held in a neighborhood Grange hall, church basement or other community building several miles distant from the high school. The advantages to this were travel convenience for the farmers, homogeneity of type of farming, and acquaintance of the men with each other. Limitations of the effectiveness of this type of adult farmers evening class stemmed from the frequent use of guest lecturers, motion picture films, or other visual aids borrowed for single meetings on topics not functionally or sequentially related. The teacher generally was paid only for the actual meeting hours and was unlikely to go to farms to provide individual instruction unless the family had a son enrolled in the high school classes in agriculture.

The economy of the nation was handicapped during the 1930–1940 period by unemployment, low wages and prices, and by surpluses of agricultural commodities. Incentives for mechanization, increase in labor efficiency, and expansion in the size of individual farm business were generated by the national emergency demands of World War II. Agricultural education leaders in many states prepared special course outlines for adult classes in major livestock and crop enterprises. A larger contribution during the years from 1941 to 1945 was made through enrollment of farmers in classes in farm machinery maintenance and repair. Agricultural equipment manufacturers turned out war goods rather than tractors and farm implements. Crop acreages were increased. Fewer laborers were available and wages were higher. These motivations were powerful. Outcomes of classes conducted by teachers of agriculture in high school farm mechanics shops were reported in numbers of power and machinery units serviced, repaired, or reconditioned. Of greater significance in long range evaluation were the educational results from the decision-making, management-oriented instruction that occurred in the courses inasmuch as the instructors not only taught agricultural mechanics skills but aided individual farm operators in adjusting their businesses to changing conditions.

The post-war veterans education and training program under the provisions of what was known as the GI Bill enrolled thousands of men whose educational objectives were to become established in farming. The following comments from the Report of the Panel of Consultants on Vocational Education will introduce certain features not previously a part of adult instruction in agriculture:

> Training courses were reviewed in relation to State criteria, and approval of on-the-job or formal school instruction was granted on the basis of these criteria. Many vocational teachers, coordinators, and supervisors were employed at all levels to staff the program and provide liaison with the Veterans Administration at State, regional and national levels. . . . Great impetus in curriculum development of many occupational training courses and programs undoubtedly

clarified teaching and learning of many traditional jobs and a host of the newer occupations.[1]

In trade and industrial education and in distributive education many training programs were set up on an on-the-job plan in which the employer provided the learning experiences for the trainee in his plant or other place of business. Formal school instruction conducted in public, private, or proprietary vocational education facilities was the government subsidized administrative arrangement in other training programs. Leaders in agricultural education who aided in designing the training pattern for agriculture combined on-the-job instruction and experience with attendance at regular classes. The instructor who taught the class, at least four hours per week, used the rest of his time visiting the adult students on the farms they operated or where they were employed and providing a planned sequence of on-the-job learning experiences. The demonstrated efficiency of the combination pattern of instruction later encouraged school districts to assign portions of day-time working hours of the teachers of agriculture to be used in individual on-farm instruction. Since enactment of the Vocational Education Act of 1963 the procedure is being applied to adult education for off-farm occupations.

Increased capital requirements in agricultural production, larger size of individual farm businesses in terms of animals units and acres of crops harvested, reduction in numbers of hired farm hands, and more complex involvements in marketing have focused attention on management as the prime educational need of persons who own and operate modern commercial farms and allied agricultural enterprises. Technical information relating to seeds, feeds, fertilizers, and agricultural chemicals is readily available from manufacturers and distributors of these supplies. Dealers in farm power and equipment have learned that it is very worth while for them to assist in instructing their farmer customers in the selection, safe operation and preventive maintenance of each tractor, implement or other item in agricultural mechanization and automation. Vertical integration in the marketing and processing of food and other agricultural products has brought another large segment of American business directly into educational relationships with farmers. Income tax

---

[1] Report of the Panel of Consultants on Vocational Education, *Education for a Changing World of Work* OE-80021 (Washington, D.C.: U.S. Government Printing Office, 1963), p. 105.

regulations have made the keeping of complete farm accounts a necessity. All of the factors just listed, and there are more, have brought management education to the forefront in curriculum planning in agriculture.

In an Office of Education bulletin prepared in collaboration with vocational educators in states with many young adult farmers enrolled in post-high school classes in agriculture, Hunsicker presented the imperative requirements for continuing education in farm business organization and management in this way:

> When young farmers leave or graduate from high school they find soon that their needs and problems have multiplied. Those who are considering farming as an occupation will have to analyze and reexamine their interests, intentions to farm, and opportunities to become established as farmers. . . . Even those fortunate enough to start with a farm, a minimum of machinery and equipment, and a will to succeed face difficult problems and choices.
>
> As young farmers progress toward successful establishment in farming, they will recognize the need for instruction in: Developing parent-son agreements in farming, renting farm land, locating available finances, producing farm products efficiently, selecting and maintaining farm equipment, marketing farm products, keeping and analyzing records, developing farm and home plans, planning land use and conservation programs, laying out crop rotation systems, interpreting government programs, interpreting and executing legal papers, making tax returns and Social Security payments, and participating in farm and community organizations. Further education and training will develop the ability of young farmers to better solve many of their perplexing problems in these areas.[2]

To implement the foregoing concepts, a number of states gave official endorsement to "the farm management approach" to adult education in agriculture. The support was in various forms. Additional agriculture instructors were hired, time of qualified teachers was assigned to adult classes including individual instruction of students, and additional state funds were allocated to schools that conducted approved programs. The instruction has earned commendation from the men enrolled, from farm organization leaders, and from citizen groups charged with responsibility for appraisal of public school occupational education.

---

[2] H. N. Hunsicker, *Planning and Conducting a Program of Instruction in Vocational Agriculture for Young Farmers,* U.S. Department of Health, Education, and Welfare, Office of Education, Voc. Div. Bul. 262 (Washington, D.C.: U.S. Government Printing Office, 1956), pp. 4–6.

The situation at present, in the mid-1960's, is such that every available technique for further improvement in management education and in technological training of commercial farm operators needs to be thoroughly applied in existing programs. An added supply of qualified teachers should be graduated to staff adult programs in more secondary schools. Specialized programs will be initiated in area vocational-technical schools as they are built with funds of the Vocational Education Act of 1963. Because most of the present vocational education programs in agriculture are located in local school districts with concentrations of commercial farms, it is likely that adult instruction in agricultural production will continue and expand in these schools. New courses for persons in off-farm agricultural occupations may become a major responsibility of the area schools.

Administrative Relationships

There may be no better evidence that a population area served by an efficient size modern secondary school system deserves to be known as an *education-oriented community* than to find that a comprehensive program of continuing adult education is in operation and enrolling, year after year, larger numbers of persons who profit from the instruction by advances in their employment status as well as in general education personal satisfactions. Having an understanding and giving approval to a basic philosophy that adults can learn and want to continue to learn is fundamental. Having an awareness that adequate physical facilities, in terms of public school buildings and equipment, are available at little extra cost is a practical consideration. Recruitment of capable instructors becomes less difficult as communities increase in proportion of residents who are college graduates and whose professional or technical employment requires that they keep up-to-date in their special fields. Finally, the chief school administrator and local board of education must be able and willing to accept leadership responsibility in organizing and administering appropriate adult programs.

In the past in rural community high schools the initiative for establishing adult classes for farmers has come from the local teachers of agriculture. They may have acted from a desire to provide the community with the quality and variety of service that had been described to them as a model in their professional training in the state universities, or they may have recognized that former high school students urgently needed continuing instruction. In addition, persuasion of state and district supervisors of vocational education in agriculture has been a stimulus to action. Not often has the influence come from a request of the school administration that agriculture be added to an already diversified set of adult course offerings. This motivation may operate in the years ahead as area vocational-technical schools are established within commuting distance of the homes and places of employment of persons in agricultural occupations.

Whether or not an instructor organizes and successfully conducts adult classes the first year of his membership on the faculty of a school may depend on his own degree of professional maturity, vision, and sense of commitment. It may be determined by the presence of an on-going program; that he fits into it is simply expected by the school and by the adult students who have profited from previous courses and long-term individual instruction and guidance. A beginning teacher whose pre-service student teaching or internship experience has been in a school where an outstanding adult education program is in operation has greater probability of early success in his own school.

Most of the details of administration may be handled according to established policies in the school. To qualify for state financial subsidies approval must be obtained from vocational education supervisors. Explanation of local need for flexibility in interpretation of standards or requirements normally results in approval being given and may cause the innovative features to be treated as a pilot program. At a future date, dissemination to other schools of procedures found to be successful may inspire further advance in the local program.

There must be students before there is an adult program. Adult vocational education in agriculture in public schools is based on voluntary enrollment. Fees charged are low. Regularity of attendance and completion of courses depends upon student appraisal of the value of the instruction. Surveying the needs of potential students, getting to know them personally, and actualy obtaining class enrollment are, therefore, essentially as much a part of administration as of instruction.

Individual Instruction

Occupational education is clearly purposeful. It is goal oriented. The first thing a teacher should do in contacting a young adult farmer is to arrange a visit to his farm. An hour or two spent in observing the nature and scope of the total business, the combination of diversified enterprises, and the likely future development of each phase of the operation is of crucial significance. The teacher should listen as the prospective adult student outlines his personal and family goals. If the young man is single and living at home with parents, they should be involved in the conference. If married, the wife is important as a participant in the planning of an individual instruction program.

While walking over the fields, the farmer can (1) discuss the selective uses of each type of soil, (2) point out conservation practices employed and changes contemplated, (3) describe yields in terms of fertilizers, varieties and pest control, and (4) indicate rotation adjustments that might be advantageous. If the man is largely unaware of the need for making decisions in management areas such as these, the instructor may profitably make mental notes of them. Written plans ultimately become part of the teaching program. If the farm has not been enrolled in the Soil Conservation Service program and had a long-term conservation and land use plan prepared by the county work unit conservationist, the owner-operator probably will welcome the advice and help of the teachers of agriculture in taking the necessary steps. A field-by-field fertility management record system can become a key element in instructional planning.

The prospective adult class member surely will want to show the visiting instructor his livestock and explain production practices including automation as it affects labor management. Production and performance records, if kept systematically, provide a measure of efficiency in terms of standards set. Dairy Herd Improvement Association records make possible selective breeding programs. When coupled with forage analyses and concentrate feeding records, an appraisal of the nutrition program is feasible. Beef, swine, sheep, and poultry performance records are equally essential in management decision-making on farms where each is a major source of income.

Capital investments in buildings, machinery and equipment must be kept in balance with needs for funds for operating expenses. Depreciations have to be weighed against savings in labor costs and in convenience and risk-insuring benefits. Electronic data-processing equipment used in newly-developed accounting systems makes available to farmers today a much more versatile system of alternative budgeting and assessment of results, including linear programming techniques. At present, instructors are right at the point of understanding the application of the procedures sufficiently to make computer-based accounting and business analysis a basic part of individual adult instruction.

Each individual visit has diagnostic and guidance values. Each is an initial period of instruction, a first phase in a complete cycle of the learning process. Considered as a group, with summarizing techniques applied, the result is a survey. Generalizations based on similarities as well as upon categorization of differences indicate areas of emphasis on educational needs that should guide the specification of subject matter for courses to be taught. Survey tabulations also reveal areas in which the instructor should concentrate his own effort to improve in competence.

The experience of teachers who make systematic surveys of groups of potential adult class members is that the men are quite willing to furnish answers to questions concerning characteristics including education, interests, and interpersonal relationships. They assume that the instructor will record, file, and study the data, as any other professional counselor would do, to determine ways to best serve the individual client. Standardized tests may be used; the men respond with great interest in their own relative performance. Such an experience in a voluntary situation is without reservations of the setting of an unemployed worker being processed through personnel testing.

The following set of items representing practices that apply to dairy, livestock or general farms has been used in the form of a rating scale as a part of systematic surveys with young adult farmers in about fifty schools. The instructor acting as interviewer asks the farmer to explain ten phases of the business. Together, instructor and student agree upon a rating for each item. The Likert-type summated rating scale values are: Excellent 5, Very Satisfactory 4, Satisfactory 3, Less than Satisfactory 2, Unsatisfactory 1, or Does Not Apply X. The items are:

1. Explain your system of farm records, farm budgeting and financing, and purchasing as carried out this year.

2. Explain your marketing practices, including sources and uses of market information, quality of products, and marketing methods used this year.

3. Explain your soil fertility, soil and water conservation, and land use program as in operation this year.

4. Explain the essential planting, fertilizing, and harvesting practices used in achieving your production efficiency goals for a major forage crop this year.

5. Explain the essential planting, fertilizing, and harvesting practices used in achieving your production efficiency goals for a major row crop or small grain this year.

6. Explain your insect, disease and weed control program for a major crop enterprise (forage, row crop, or small grain) this year.

7. Explain the essential breeding, feeding, and management practices used in achieving your production efficiency goals for a major livestock enterprise this year.

8. Explain your health management program for a major live stock enterprise this year.

9. Explain your program for selection, operation, and mainte- nance of farm power, machinery and equipment this year.

10. Explain your building construction and remodeling pro- gram in relation to labor management practices and to size and type of production enterprises this year.

It is an effective teaching procedure to repeat the survey with each student at intervals of one or two years. The reappraisal yields sat- isfaction in specific achievements and draws attention to unfulfilled needs or goals not yet attained. Decisions can be made to adjust the class instruction program if summarization of ratings reveals no significant advance in areas of previously less than adequate per- formance.

Where individual instruction is given the type of instruction must be determined by what is to be learned. Skills that require teacher demonstration and student practice usually are taught on the farm in the actual job situation. This applies primarily to livestock and crop production practices. Many skills in agricultural mechanics may be learned in the school shop, often by practicing on farm equipment brought to the school for a few days by men enrolled in the class.

More than half of the instructor-adult student contact hours during a twelve-month period are likely to be used for discussion of management decisions. Teachers generally time their trips to farms not at hours of regular care of livestock or, unless a problem is urgent, on days of peak activity in field crop operations. As better record systems evolve, conferences with the adult agriculture instructor logically can be held at the farmer's desk, the business control center of his total operation. It may be located in the home or in the office that is part of a year-round air-conditioned farm service center.

There is a definitely growing trend toward adult at-the-school individual instruction. Self-employed farmers and persons in other off-farm agricultural businesses who have managerial responsibilities are finding it convenient and desirable to schedule appointments with the instructor at his office at the school. Often the instructional visit may be combined with another need, such as a supplies pick-up, a sales delivery, or a trip to the bank. The student should bring essential records with him. There is the advantage of ready access to the agricultural library resources of the school. The instructor is a professional; confidences are inviolate. The values of individual conferences to each adult student increase from year to year as the instructor gains in understanding of each man's educational needs.

The continuing adult education relationship with vocational educators in agriculture in the schools of a community may extend through the lifetime of the individual. This has often been the parallel situation in cooperative agricultural and home economics extension. It has been so in high school areas where effective teachers have had long tenure. But, much more has been written about how a young man may acquire a farm or other agricultural business *from* an owner than about the adjustments necessary to be made *by* the man who is approaching or who has reached retirement age. Byram had the following to say about adult guidance of older workers:

> In the last decade educators generally have become more aware of their responsibilities to those on retirement or nearing retirement. This is due in part to the growing proportion of the population who are of this age. Many questions about Social Security have arisen in farmers' minds, not so much dealing with legal and financial as-

pects as with their own personal plans and adjustments. It is not yet clear just what kind of help the teachers of agriculture could most appropriately give through consultation with retiring or retired farmers, but this problem should merit further study.[3]

To conclude this section on individual instruction of adults, the point of view is repeated that courses to be taught should arise from the common needs of perhaps ten to twenty or more adult students. It is evident that individual instruction may follow class teaching perhaps as often as individual consultations in advance of the course have helped to structure the class sessions. In fact, it is conceivable that students enroll in and attend the classes to establish and maintain the individual instruction relationship. The best local school vocational programs of agricultural education for adults have differed in at least two significant ways from the conventional stereotype of marginal offerings of unrelated one semester adult classes taught by adjunct instructors. Continuous year after year individual and class procedures and course content are adjusted to successively higher levels of achievement of persons who remain active participants and who share in planning and other phases of class organization. The instructors are regular full-time employees in established departments of schools that formally recognize occupational placement and adjustment as an institutional function and proudly appraise and report student employment, promotions, and other advances in education and status.

Class Teaching

The reasons why people attend voluntary, non-college credit adult classes are important to administrators, to coordinators of adult education programs, to instructors who must select the learning activities and use the most effective teaching procedures. Not least, they ought to be understood by the students themselves. Jensen and others[4] explained that the first interest of youth education in the schools is in socializing the child, and that the adult educator

---

[3] Byram, H. M., *Guidance in Agricultural Education*, (Danville, Ill.: The Interstate Printers and Publishers, Inc., 1966), p. 188.

[4] Jensen, Gale, A. A. Liveright, Wilbur Hallenbeck, eds., *Adult Education: Outlines of an Emerging Field of University Study,* (Chicago, Ill.: Adult Education Association of America, 1964).

faces the task of re-socializing the adult. They observed that in a static traditional society adult education is redundant; there is no need to change social roles or acquire new skills. In our society, technological change demands new skills and shapes human relationships; social mobility permits and encourages changes in status, in values, and in social relationships; geographical mobility generates necessity for adaptations to different modes of living and to new economic situations. The worlds of the adult, in general order or priority, are the world of work, the social world, the world of form, and the world of nature. Vocational education skills can be clearly specified and thus efficiently learned. Social competencies need real settings, also, in which to be developed. The liberally educated adult whose occupation is in agriculture and whose social world is rural America surely will profit from conscious attention to appreciations of form and nature.

Mason and Haines[5] stated that for out-of-school youth and adults increased job competency in their present occupations or preparation for different employment comes to some degree from on-the-job training, but increasingly it comes from organized courses offered by schools and by employers and their trade and professional associations. A basic approach to program planning in adult education is the analysis of people and their occupational needs. Individuals, at one time or another in their lifetime, may need continuing adult education in preparation for a new occupation, to increase performance in the present job, in preparation for advancement, or as retraining made necessary by a variety of factors. Needs may be classified by job level into employee, supervisory, and management. Mason and Haines continued their discussion of the "needs approach" with the following:

> The coordinator engaged in adult education should be aware that some adults enroll in vocational classes to meet needs not expressed in the occupational classification already discussed. A great many people enroll to satisfy needs such as the desire to associate with other people in the same occupations; the need for stimulation to their thinking; the wish to increase status with fellow employees, supervisors, friends, and family, which comes with increasing their

---

[5] Mason, Ralph E., Peter G. Haines, *Cooperative Occupational Education and Work Experience in the Curriculum,* (Danville, Ill.: The Interstate Printers and Publishers, Inc., 1965), pp. 300–302.

educational level; or the desire to gain certificates attesting to their accomplishments.[6]

Education is a function of the state. As such in a free society, it is intended to serve the purposes of the individual as well as the imperatives of the group. Individual investment of time, funds, and other resources are as much an obligation of the citizen as of government. Morgan, Holmes, and Bundy[7] said that some believe that adult learning experiences should be separated into one type labelled "adult education" and another that may be called "the education of the adult." The employment of agriculture instructors to teach courses for adult students is primarily concerned with what may be termed formal adult education. Wise planning will take into account the many informal sources of educative experiences that have shaped the personality of the individual and that should be not only passively accepted but actively built into supporting roles as teaching plans are developed. In many states supervisors and teacher educators prepare resource units as suggested guides to instructors as they perform the professional function of preparation of courses they are to teach.

Hunsicker prefaced a detailed exposition of methods and techniques that have been proven to be effective in young adult farmer classes with these statements:

> Good teaching and having members [of the class] share in the responsibility for group meetings are key factors to success in working with young farmers. An interested group of young men have been recruited, challenging objectives may have been established, and a well-planned calendar of instruction developed—yet all this work, as essential as it may be, is only preliminary to helping young farmers solve their problems. Good teaching must follow. The young farmers will need to be inspired to act and trained to make those decisions and to perform those skills in managing and operating their farms that will enable them to be successful. . . .[8]

There are certain essentials in a teaching plan. The total unit of instruction should be clearly specified and its component problem

[6] *Ibid.*, p. 302.

[7] Barton Morgan, Glenn E. Holmes, Clarence E. Bundy, *Methods in Adult Education,* (Danville, Ill.: The Interstate Printers and Publishers, Inc., 1963), pp. 48–52.

[8] Hunsicker, *op. cit.*, p. 31.

areas delineated. The number of class sessions to be devoted to each area or topic must be determined, subject to modification during the course as progress of the group is found to be faster or slower than anticipated. The session topics or lessons should be arranged in psychological sequence. Self-evaluation devices should be used as an integral part of the learning process. With appropriate consideration for the much greater experience background of mature students, the principles of learning outlined in Chapter IV for use with high school classes apply to adult groups. Group discussion techniques are admirably suited to management problems. Demonstrations and field trips reduce misunderstanding of unfamiliar terms and confusion caused by imprecise verbalization. Chapter VI will emphasize the great variety of instructional resources available to teachers of agriculture and show how they are used in class instruction.

The Young Farmers Association

Leadership development is a very important adult education objective. Participating experiences are required to achieve it. Each individual must have real responsibilities in situations that involve personal and group goals that have value and meaning. Co-curricular activities in high school are desirable but limited to the type of social control in which teachers and parents occupy an authoritative role. A local school Young Farmers Association whose members are the persons enrolled in the post-high school classes in agriculture today serves important leadership training functions in many communities in an increasing number of states. Ohio, Virginia, Pennsylvania, Texas, Utah, California, South Carolina, and some others have had more than ten years experience with state associations of affiliated local units, that may be called chapters. Membership is open to everyone enrolled in the adult education program in agriculture in the school.

The Young Farmers Association operates with a set of by-laws, has a definite officer and committee structure, and prepares and carries out a written annual program of activities.[9] Prominent in the goals of the organization are items that support the program of class instruction; the activities relate to ways in which the members may

---

[9] *Handbook, The Pennsylvania Young Farmers Association* (Harrisburg, Pa.: Department of Public Instruction, 1965), pp. 18–25.

assist the teachers of agriculture with their instructional responsibilities. The Association may raise funds for teaching materials. Committees are assigned to obtain services of resource persons. Arrangements for transportation on field trips and tours are handled by the students. The executive committee is a very fine department advisory council. In a growing frequency of instances, one member accepts responsibility for individual instruction of another. This is a planned aid to diffusion of improved practices and new knowledge in the community.

A young adult student organization is related to individual on-farm or on-the-job instruction more in terms of its contribution to improved family and community living than as a requirement in instruction that leads to advance in occupational skill and efficiency. A Young Farmers Association program of work generally includes community service activities, cooperative activities and social and recreational activities. Wives of the members participate in some of the projects, meetings and events. Training received frequently results in the young farmer becoming a member and leader in state and national farm organizations and in regional civic groups.

Technician Education in Agriculture

Courses for persons employed in off-farm occupations where knowledge of agricultural subject matter is useful may be organized as a part of the adult education programs of comprehensive high schools and area vocational-technical schools in much the same manner as young farmer classes have been conducted. For many such persons the courses should provide technician education. A major difference in employment situation is that, unlike young farmers who are in the process of achieving owner-operator status, most of the potential students are wage or salary employees. The individual on-the-job phase of the instructional relationship is like that of cooperative education or work experience as in trade and industrial or distributive education programs. These vocational education services have called the instructor a coordinator, meaning that he coordinates the instruction the learner receives from the employer with the school activities. Agriculture must staff its new technician level programs in off-farm occupational specializations with highly qualified coordinators. This calls for not only advanced college preparation of the teachers but also for them to have experience in the technical occupations in agricultural business and industry.

Having used reference to the pre-eminent position of the United States in the economical production of food and fiber and used the impact of great technological change in only the last few years to show the imperative need for highly skilled, progressive, and well-trained leaders and supporting personnel to maintain and advance our present position of unequaled efficiency, Brooking and Hunsicker defined the work of the agricultural technician by using comparative illustrations from other vocational education fields:

> In agriculture, as in other fields, the highly skilled technician is becoming an increasingly important member of the scientific and management team in modern research, development, production, and service. The team is comprised of professional (agricultural) scientists, specially trained technicians, supervisors, and skilled production or laboratory workers.
>
> Technicians are trained for employment in the physical science and engineering-related fields of electronics, mechanical design and control, civil and construction technology, chemistry and metallurgy. Others enter the life science fields, including medical and dental laboratory technology and nursing, as well as agricultural production and research. More technicians are needed in the applied biological, agricultural and allied life science technologies.
>
> The explosion of new knowledge has caused changes in scientific education so that the recently graduated professional scientist or engineer often has had little laboratory experience, and he functions more as a theoretical scientist than in the past. Thus, there is a gap in the area of applied laboratory knowledge that was formerly the domain of the scientist or engineer which is being increasingly filled by highly trained technicians.[10]

Brooking, Technical Education Specialist, and Hunsicker, Chief, Agricultural Education Service, both of the U.S. Office of Education, continued by stating that agricultural technicians work in the following types of activity:

1. *Research and development* in all branches of science and engineering as they are applied to agricultural problems.

2. *Production and related processing and marketing* of agricultural crops and products; also the culture and conservation of

---

[10] Brooking, Walter J., H. N. Hunsicker, "More Skilled Agricultural Technicians Are Needed," *Agricultural Education Magazine*, XXXVIII, No. 12 (June, 1966), 276.

soil, forests, wildlife, grasslands, inland waters, and other agricultural resources.

3. *Distribution and servicing* of machinery and equipment, of supplies such as seed, feed, fertilizer, feeding or breeding stock, pesticides, and other sources as needed for production, processing, and marketing of farm products.

In the planning of programs for educating agricultural technicians, the *agricultural* or closely related occupational competencies must be identified and made the stated objectives of the program. . . . Primary emphasis should be on the underlying sciences and related technical study of procedures, processes, techniques, methods and principles. The courses should include extensive laboratory experience and should be application oriented. Each curriculum should provide courses in mathematics to the degree necessary to support the science. It should include courses in communications and technical reporting and courses which provide pertinent understanding of the applicable principles of economics, business management and cost control, and human relationships.[11]

The sequence of the subjects in a two-year technician education program should be such that first courses in agricultural specializations are taught in the first term. Many students need stimulation to sustain interest that might be lacking if, as is customary in baccalaureate programs, the first year consisted entirely of mathematics, English, social studies and introductory science. Inductively, students may be motivated to greater depth of understanding of principles as well as to higher degrees of skill application by second level courses in the essential specializations in the later semesters or terms.

Clark and Oliver,[12] in reporting on completion of a contract of the Bureau of Adult and Vocational Education, U.S. Office of Education, with the Grain and Feed Dealers Association to prepare a suggested two-year post-high school curriculum guide, arranged twenty courses into a four-semester sequence of increasing demand for management and scientific understanding. They placed "very strong emphasis on the need for occupational experience as part of

---

11 *Ibid.,* pp. 276–279.
12 Raymond M. Clark, Alvin E. Oliver, "Post-High School Curriculum for the Grain, Feed, Seed and Farm Supply Industry," *Agricultural Education Magazine* XXXIX, No. 5 (November, 1966), pp. 108–110.

the training program." A committee of grain and feed industry leaders felt that their association and others would be happy to cooperate in providing occupational experience while the students were in the training program. They expect that the experience in their plants and stores will be well planned and well coordinated by teachers who understand and can perform capably in the occupations involved as current practice requires.

The number of specialized technician education programs must be limited in each state. Similarly, the number of universities that offer teacher education programs in each area need not be large. Divisions of four-year colleges with strong degree and research programs have the facilities and staff to offer technician education. Community colleges and technical institutes are the institutions in which greatest growth in new programs is taking place. Area vocational-technical high schools as well as many comprehensive high schools should expand their orientation toward preparation of students to enter technical education majors either in the last two years of high school or immediately following graduation.

Brooking and Hunsicker[13] pointed out that to add curriculums for agricultural technician training in an institution that already offers some programs is usually less expensive than starting such courses where no technical education is being offered. Much laboratory equipment for biological sciences may be utilized. The library and its staff already exist and need only the addition of the agriculture-related information. Instructors of communications skills, economics, human relations and other supporting courses are present and have only to adapt to the degree needed. These specialists concluded with the following reference to inservice classes for employed adults:

> The establishment of high quality programs for educating technicians pays an extra dividend by providing facilities for up-grading programs for employed adults on a part-time or evening basis. Experience has shown that most schools which offer these programs enroll a larger number of already-employed adults in such special courses than they do full-time young people in preparatory technician programs.[14]

---

13 Brooking, Hunsicker, *op. cit.,* p. 281.
14 *Ibid.*

As a final note, it is appropriate to refer to adult guidance and placement services. Employment predictions for the next decade are that most agricultural businesses and industries will need more new workers with one or two years of post-high school technical education than will be prepared by the institutions that can be established within the next several years. In addition, most present employees will require advanced instruction to maintain job effectiveness.

CHAPTER VI

Instructional Resources

Teachers of agriculture have ready access to a splendid variety and quality of resources which they can use effectively in both class and individual instruction. These resources might be classified as people, places, and things. The people are farmers, managers and employees in off-farm agricultural businesses and industries, and many other citizens whose professional, technical and leadership competencies are generously contributed when the teacher explains a learning situation in which his students need specific help. The places are farms, business establishments, classrooms, agricultural mechanics shops, and conference-office-laboratory areas at the school. The things are farm animals, crops, buildings, machinery, supplies, research and measurement devices, libraries, texts and references, periodicals, films, slides, television, radio, and other learning aids.

Farmers and Their Farms

In a majority of the larger agricultural states, a typical community that offers vocational-technical instruction in agriculture is likely to have one hundred or more commercial farms with gross product receipts of over ten thousand dollars and a few at least twice that size. Several high school graduates each year are required eventually to replace owner-operators of these farms. An equal number will find permanent employment in off-farm agricultural positions. Some are needed to migrate to communities that do not teach agriculture. Part-time employment while attending school helps the farmers to meet demands of peak labor periods and provides experience for students.

The nation has experienced a century of successful cooperation of farmers, universities, and government in research and education. For a half century this relationship has included high school vocational education in agricultural production. Farmers have profited from method and result demonstrations carried out in the setting of

86

their practical management and control. They have responded to requests that their farms be used for field trips by school classes. Many instructors efficiently use such farms; some employ an alternative of school-owned and operated land laboratories.

Agricultural Business and Industry

Prior to the National Vocational Education Act of 1963, with its authorization of programs for any occupation needing knowledge and skills in agricultural subjects, teachers were accustomed to asking owners, managers and technical specialists in agricultural business and industry to assist in instruction of farmers. The orientation was the application of science and business principles to farming. The businessmen benefited indirectly as the farmers purchased larger volumes of supplies or marketed larger quantities of products. Often a local manager could call in a company fieldman, a professional person, for consultation on the farm of a student or to assist in certain class teaching. Booklets, films, specimen materials or exhibits usually have been furnished at no cost to the school.

The emerging pattern of utilization of the instructional resources of the agricultural industry other than farming is chiefly slanted in the direction of cooperative work experience for high school students and for employed adults. Teachers must have had or must be required to obtain an amount of experience in the special business area that qualifies them to teach and to supervise trainees who can enter available technical positions and perform required duties at current levels of knowledge in the business. Feed, seed, fertilizer, agricultural chemical, and equipment suppliers need technically trained young men. Some will become assistant managers. Education beyond high school is virtually a necessity, but the positions need not be filled by four-year college graduates. It would be unwise, often financially prohibitive, for a school to attempt to duplicate the real working environment. Hence, it is most fortunate that cooperative training plans have been successfully developed.

Agencies, Professions, and Services

Agencies of the Department of Agriculture, and of other divisions of the federal and state governments, engage in continuous efforts to educate citizens, consumers as well as producers. An agency welcomes a request by a school for aid in carrying out instruction related to the agency's function in public welfare. Agency employees often have been college classmates of the instructors. A kind of team teaching results, with benefits for all.

In agricultural education, professional persons are those who have earned college degrees. A doctoral level education is increasingly required as preparation for scientists who head research and development departments of major corporations in the agricultural industry. Most of them can be persuaded to devote some of their time giving educational assistance to schools that train technicians. University professors not only are responsible for undergraduate and graduate education of teachers; they can be outstandingly effective in answering inservice requests to visit teachers at their schools to help in teaching a unit that needs a revised, up-to-date approach. The privately employed professional group, including veterinarians, economists, lawyers, bankers, accountants, represent another local instructional resource.

Organizations that perform agricultural testing and quality control services are of great importance to teachers. How to state a problem may be determined by the nature and significance of results of quality tests of soil, plant tissues, fruits, animals and animal products and diagnostic tests of power units and mechanical equipment. Record keeping, business programming and analysis services are teaching aids.

There are school services that support the program in agricultural education. Libraries, computers, secretarial departments, transportation and science laboratories are some of them. Particular mention should be made of school guidance services. Byram summarized their value to teachers in these statements:

> Above all, the development of competency in guidance includes the development of ability to use the resources of the school and community. The competent teacher who does not have the answer to a question knows where the answer can be found. He knows who the persons are who have the information or help, and how they can be reached. He knows not just the resources of the local community, but of the county and state as well, or he knows where he can find out about these resources. The teacher of agriculture who is competent in guidance is one who is skillful in identifying needs, who can plan and organize activities related to these needs, and

who has the ability to draw on help from whatever source is available to meet these needs.[1]

The Agriculture Classroom

Flexibility of arrangement of student tables, chairs and other equipment is a dominant feature of classrooms for high school and adult classes in agriculture. Ample shelves, cabinets and other types of storage space for reference materials, bound and unbound, neatly occupy interior wall areas or are located in adjacent storage rooms. It is desirable to have the classroom one-and-one half standard units in size. This accommodates exhibits, demonstrations, role-playing efforts, and allows physical separation for huddle group or committee work activities. Built in convenience outlets and other structural details promote efficient use of all modern types of audiovisual media.

Reorganized secondary schools and area vocational-technical schools are of sufficient size that the numbers of students who should have instruction in agriculture make the employment of two or more instructors a necessity. This influences the physical facilities needed. In more new schools there will be two classrooms for agriculture. Each should have doors that lead into school corridors and may need exits through the conference-office-laboratory room or agricultural mechanics shop to the parking lot that serves the department. Traffic control and noise suppression are important matters. Arrangement of rooms, insulation, school-quality carpet on classroom floor and in office areas, solid walls rather than excessive use of glass partitions and other architectural details improve the general atmosphere and satisfaction of all who use the facilities.

The Agricultural Mechanics Shop

Unquestionably the most distinctive feature of most agriculture departments is the shop. It has served primarily for instruction of farmers in the selection, safe operation, maintenance and repair of agricultural production machinery and equipment. As additional specialized programs for off-farm agricultural occupations are or-

---

[1] Byram, H. M., *Guidance in Agricultural Education* (Danville, Ill.: The Interstate Printers and Publishers, Inc., 1966), p. 249.

ganized, adjustments in the teaching of mechanics principles and practices appropriate to supplies merchandising, products marketing, ornamental horticulture services, and resources management will be made. The first precaution in designing a shop is to be sure that it is large enough to allow for adaptation to new emphases.

Hollenberg and Johnson assembled detailed suggestions for many construction features that contribute to superior instruction in agricultural mechanics, among which are:

> The shop is preferably an integral part of the same structure in which the classroom is located, and is deserving of the same consideration as to esthetics, engineering, and economics in the selection of building materials, architectural design, and equipment, . . . Two features are of paramount importance: (1) large areas of unobstructed floor space, and (2) easy access provided for large farm machines or other projects to and from the shop. Agricultural mechanics shops vary in size, but 40 feet is a minimum width. A width to length ratio not greater than 1 to 2 is desirable.
>
> It is important that the ceiling in a shop be high enough to provide headroom for large farm equipment. . . . Usually a 14-foot ceiling will be adequate. . . . The entry door should be 14 to 16 feet wide, preferably of the overhead type.[2]

Many other features were listed by Hollenberg and Johnson. Several states maintain regularly revised lists of equipment for agricultural mechanics. Some stress the economy of fenced-in and partly-roofed outdoor storage areas, an unloading ramp, color dynamics, other safety measures including special welding, spray painting and steam-cleaning areas.

The Conference-Office-Laboratory Area

In the modern concept of adequate housing for a complete program of vocational-technical education in agriculture an area nearly equal in square feet of floor space to that of the classroom is needed for conference, office, and laboratory functions. Adult students make frequent use of such a combination room or area during daytime hours when high school classes are meeting in the regular classroom and shop. A farmer or agricultural businessman may stop at

---

[2] Hollenberg, A. H. and E. J. Johnson, *Buildings, Equipment, and Facilities for Vocational Agriculture Education.* OE-81003 U.S. Office of Education (Washington, D.C.: Government Printing Office, 1960), pp. 32 ff.

the school to keep an individual appointment with the instructor of the night class the man is attending. He meets the teacher at his office. When a committee of adults or of high school students decides to work on a class or student leadership activity, they should know that the conference table area is available to them. Any student may arrange to do individual testing of soil, seed, grain or other crops, milk or other livestock products, or to use desk calculators and other office machines in the laboratory area. Planning activities for work to be done in the shop may be more conveniently worked on in the conference room located between the classroom and the shop. Other facilities such as a greenhouse (*see page* 38) or food technology laboratory are required for specialized programs.

Teaching Materials

Obtaining, filing, and using government and university bulletins and circulars is a continuing responsibility of teachers of agriculture. Valuable publications also are available at no cost from agricultural businesses and industries. Instructors should encourage each student to accumulate a personal library of selected materials from these sources. If the teacher can order a new supply in anticipation of each time a publication will be needed with a new class, the copies may be given to the students rather than retained at the school as texts or references.

Motion picture films usually are borrowed from film libraries or commercial organizations. Slides, overhead transparencies, charts, and some exhibit materials may be borrowed, but usually these items are produced by the teachers and students. Fresh specimen materials needed in laboratory demonstrations are obtainable on farms and in the community. Less frequently today is it desirable or necessary to preserve, mount, or otherwise retain such teaching aids. To take the class on a field trip to the farm or other business where the supplies or products are used may usually be most efficient.

CHAPTER VII

Administration and Supervision

To consider the concept of effective administration of public education programs is to think of the able, experienced persons charged with responsibility for school control and the multiplicity of decisions that have to be made. Existing programs must be maintained, adjusted, improved and extended. New programs require organization, initiation, and development. Administrators command respect because of the functions of the office which include regulation, inspection, allocation of funds and physical resources, selection and assignment of staff personnel, and the execution of policies and systematized procedures.

Supervision, as a concept, may be thought of as the supporting, cooperative, consultative relationship of a group leader with each classroom teacher in his charge. The supervisor was first a successful instructor, has continued to maintain technical subject matter competence and, in addition, has leadership skill that inspires each teacher with whom he works to higher levels of performance. A supervisor often has some administrative duties. In large school systems it is less likely that administrators assume supervisory roles.

The administration of vocational-technical education in the United States starts at the federal level because there are federal funds to be allocated to the states; to qualify for the funds each state must meet the set of standards in the enabling legislation. The state is a level of administration. There may be a county or other type of intermediate unit. Area vocational-technical schools, technical institutes, community or junior colleges, and non-baccalaureate divisions of four-year colleges are special types of administrative units. The local school district is by far the most frequent administrative organization in which vocational education programs are operated.

Functions of the U.S. Office of Education

The Agricultural Education Service is one of the State Vocational Services in the Division of Vocational and Technical Education administered by the Associate Commissioner for Adult and Vocational Education in the U.S. Office of Education. The staff members, men who had prior experience as teachers of agriculture and as state supervisors, review and approve the sections of state plans concerned with their special field. They design and disseminate reporting forms, receive state reports, and check expenditures against approved program classifications in the state plan. By having regional staff employees in assigned geographic locations, visits to states are facilitated. Regional conferences for state administrators serve to disseminate information and regulations and also promote leadership development.

The Vocational Education Act of 1963 provides for the establishment of an Advisory Committee to the Commissioner of Education that shall prepare general regulations with respect to policy matters arising in the administration of the Act. The Agricultural Education Service has an advisory committee to aid in developing guidelines and program activities and priorities. An Advisory Council on Vocational Education appointed by the Secretary of Department of Health, Education, and Welfare has responsibility for periodic review of the administration of federal vocational education programs and for making recommendations. Cooperation of states and local districts results in individual decisions making for appropriate changes.

Maintaining liaison and developing working relationships with other sections of the Office of Education and divisions of the Department of Health, Education, and Welfare as well as with the Bureau of Employment Security, Department of Labor, the many directly related divisions of the Departments of Agriculture, Commerce, and Interior, and other government agencies are very valuable functions of the professional staff of the Agricultural Education Service. Long-range projects involving major agricultural industries, trade associations, and farm organizations will increase in number and scope. Education is interested in increasing the employability of youth and adults; business and industry must have adequately trained workers. Meetings sponsored by the Office of Education serve to initiate mutually beneficial action. As examples, the Farm-Industrial Equipment Institute has prepared a set of policies encouraging its manufacturers and dealers to make their many educational publications and other resources easily available to vocational-technical schools. On contract with the Office of Education, the National Grain and Feed Dealers Association prepared a curriculum guide for a two-year post-high school program in agricultural supplies education.

Responsibilities of the State Education Department

Each state has a State Director of Vocational and Technical Education. In forty-two states the State Board of Education is the policy-making body for vocational-technical programs in secondary schools. Administration of post-secondary, community college, and junior college programs often is separately handled and may not be as clearly legislated. The State Supervisor of Agricultural Education performs both administrative and supervisory duties. His office assists the State Director by approving local and area programs, making allocations of state and federal funds, and providing for teacher education including recruitment and certification. Encouragement of the development of pilot projects and of systematic research programs will increase as the system of state Research Coordinating Units expands in the years ahead.

On the state level, the supervisor and his assistants carry out the functions listed under the previous section which discussed the federal service. The activities of the Future Farmers of America organization in each state are supervised by the state staff. The state supervisor is the state FFA advisor. Similar services are provided for the adult student organizations. In some states there are Young Farmers Associations. Post-high school and adult classes for off-farm agricultural technician education are forming leadership organizations and asking for counsel and assistance of state supervisors.

A planned program of inservice education of teachers of agriculture is one of the most significant responsibilities of the state education department. The number of assistant or district supervisors should be sufficient to allow several visits per year to each local and area school. Teachers welcome help with goal-setting and program planning and appreciate periodic follow-up visits to discuss evaluation of achievements. Inservice education courses for teachers may be arranged cooperatively with the teacher education staff in agricultural education in the state universities.

Services of Area Vocational-Technical Schools

High quality preparatory education of high school students for careers in agricultural production (farming) has been generally available in rural areas of the United States. The changing requirements of the future make clear the necessity for specialized education for increasing numbers of rural-reared youth and rural-resident adults. A quality general education program is possible in a small school, but financial resources cannot support specialized occupational education, particularly for post-high school students and adults. Student potential is insufficient in single, small districts. A committee of the American Vocational Association made the following explanation:

> The area program concept is a constructive and practical approach to providing adequate vocational and technical education. Area programs have two outstanding characteristics. They provide training which leads to employment, upgrading, and updating in specific occupations, and they serve students from more than one community or school district.
>
> Area programs now in existence exhibit a diversity of administrative control, financial structure, enrollments, expenditures, course offerings and services. There is no single pattern to identify the area program except that it embraces more than a single community or school district. As defined by the Vocational Education Act of 1963, an area vocational school may be:
>
> 1. A specialized high school used exclusively or almost so to provide full-time vocational education in preparation for full-time work in industry.
>
> 2. A department of a high school used exclusively or principally to provide training in at least five different occupational fields to students available for full-time study prior to entering the labor market.
>
> 3. A technical or vocational school providing vocational education predominantly to persons who have completed or left school and who are able to study on a full-time basis before going to work.
>
> 4. A department or division of a junior college, community college, or university providing vocational education in at least five different occupational fields, under the supervision of the state board of vocational education, and leading to immediate employment but not towards a baccalaureate degree.[1]

---

[1] *Area Vocational Education Programs.* (Washington, D.C.: American Vocational Association, Inc., 1966), pp. 4–5.

Area schools may be administered directly as state schools, by a county or several counties, or by one or more local school districts. They may be shared-time high school training centers to which students are transported while continuing to be enrolled in a "home high school," they may be a department in a comprehensive high school (as defined in 2 above), or they may be self-contained vocational-technical high schools offering general education as in any comprehensive high school. In each of these types of high school organization it is not only possible but highly desirable that adult education be offered. In agriculture, this makes possible specialized, advanced agricultural production courses as well as training for adults employed in off-farm agricultural occupations. It will be desirable in rural area schools to have an associate administrator whose occupational background and teaching experience have been in agriculture. It will also be an efficient use of outstanding agriculture teachers now employed in comprehensive local high schools to hire them part-time at the area school to instruct classes in specialized subjects in which each man is expert.

Area schools have distinct advantages in technician level education in agriculture in the availability of supporting subjects in business, distribution, mechanics, and related science, mathematics, communications and personnel management. For rural persons who choose to organize their careers to include employment in two occupations, each on a part-time basis or at different seasons of the year, accessibility to area school training in agriculture and in a non-agricultural occupation has appeal. Finally, for those who are to migrate to cities to live and to develop careers, the following is pertinent:

> Rural youth, in large percentages, are leaving the farm for cities and towns to seek jobs in business and industry. It is well known that most of these young people will leave (or have left) their high schools unprepared for their life's work simply because the majority of rural and small community high schools have provided only a limited curriculum in both general and vocational education. Quite often youth and adults from rural areas enter the labor market at the lowest unskilled levels; their potential productive powers are consequently lost to the nation. Area vocational and technical programs with their diversified offerings can extend training opportunities to rural youth comparable to those in larger communities and thus save this lost manpower.[2]

---

[2] *Ibid.,* p. 5.

The residential type of public-supported area vocational-technical school can serve well several groups of young people. For those who do not live within commuting distance of an area school, campus living is the alternative to excessive time and cost of daily travel. When combined with work-study or cooperative education arrangements, the residential school makes possible the attainment of technical education by boys and girls from low-income and otherwise disadvantaged situations. Further, "the residential vocational and technical school offers the student the benefits of campus life, gives him the prestige of going away to school, tends to enhance the value of vocational education in the parental mind, and has many other advantages."[3]

Community colleges and technical institutes offer two-year programs that differ from junior college programs in that they are not the first two years leading to a baccalaureate degree. Communities all over the nation are seriously considering the establishment and expansion of such institutions. A major goal is to make education beyond high school available to an additional twenty to thirty percent of all boys and girls and to look toward utilization of staff and facilities for continuing adult education in general and occupational subjects. Citizens welcome appointment to planning and advisory committees.

The importance of placement of those who complete vocational-technical programs of study cannot be overemphasized. Venn[4] recommends that schools should have a placement office with a full-time placement officer, just as do colleges. He would have the placement office of a high school or area school survey job opportunities in the area, arrange interviews for students with prospective employers, and obtain jobs for its graduates. There should be close working relationships with employers, with labor unions, and with local offices of the State Employment Service. School records should be comprehensive on all students and follow-up studies should be made continuously.

---

[3] *Ibid.,* p. 13.
[4] Grant Venn, "Occupational Education, A Lifetime Concern," *American Vocational Journal* 41:8 (November, 1966), pp. 16–17.

Duties of the Local School District

Local school administrators have primary responsibility to recognize the importance of education for work as an integral part of the general education development of most students. They need to strive for optimum emphasis on employability in achieving balance in the curriculum between general education and occupational preparation. Vocational and technical education must be provided in earlier school years to serve to reduce dropout rates before high school graduation. Ways must be found to pay the higher costs of vocational and technical education. Better teachers, more efficient use of instructor time and of student time, reduction of depreciation on buildings and equipment through wise selection, purchasing, and careful maintenance, and larger enrollments per program are administrative controls.

Local schools that have successful programs of agricultural education should strive continuously to understand the objectives and the factors that make the student achievements praiseworthy. At times it may be necessary to be prepared to defend the program. If the school has only one agriculture instructor and, like many communities, should employ two or three teachers, the administration should prepare to adjust budgets, facilities, and scheduling in anticipation of local board approval of the expansion.

School relations, community relations, filing of reports, participation in periodic department evaluation, consultation with visiting supervisors, involvement in activities of students in the agriculture classes—these are duties of local school administrators. One other important administrative responsibility is to offer constructive advice and suggestions, to ask leading questions, and to show the agriculture teacher, the citizens advisory council for the department program and the students that a dynamic community needs well educated persons in its agricultural industry.

Activities of Teachers of Agriculture

In multi-teacher departments the most experienced and most capable agriculture instructor should serve as chairman or head. Formal administrative activities should be performed by this person. They include the coordination of program planning, scheduling, assignment of shared duties, keeping of records and filing of required reports. Management of the department budget for equipment and supplies, inventory taking, attention to safety regulations, security of property, and related compliance responsibilities are delegated to the instructors by the local school person serving as vocational director or by the secondary principal.

Policy determination may be shared with the department consulting committee or advisory council subject to approval by the school administrator and school board. Execution of programs within the guidelines of a written policy statement and an annual plan is the responsibility of the agriculture teachers. In doing so, they should keep the school administration informed and report regularly to the district or state supervisor of agricultural education. Student personnel records should be kept up-to-date and in standard form so that they have maximum use in individual occupational guidance and placement and also to be of maximum usefulness to instructors who will succeed the current staff.

CHAPTER VIII

Teacher Education, Research, and Evaluation

Teacher education, research, and evaluation are important adjuncts to state programs of vocational and technical education. In the language of the Vocational Education Act of 1963 they are ancillary services to assure quality in all vocational programs. It has been general practice in the states to charge the state supervisor of each vocational field (agriculture, office and business, distributive, home economics, health, trade and industrial, and technical) with the responsibility to delegate and to supervise or to carry out the needed functions in these areas. The trend is toward unification, thus achieving better utilization of the talents of highly qualified specialists in teacher education, in research, and in local program evaluation.

University Programs for the Preparation of Teachers of Agriculture

In most states the land-grant university, where the state college of agriculture is located, has been designated by the state board for vocational education to receive funds for support of an approved program for preparation of teachers of agriculture. The functions that are to be performed, standards for training offered, and qualifications of teacher educators are specified in the state plan for vocational and technical education. Occupational competency and professional skill in teaching are required of all persons who are issued certificates or credentials approving them to be hired in positions in schools where the salaries are reimbursed from state and federal vocational funds. In agriculture it has been assumed that farm-reared high school graduates, especially if they have had high school instruction in agriculture and employment in agricultural positions in the summers between college terms, are occupationally experienced and need primarily the agricultural science and professional education courses to qualify as beginning teachers. The general and liberal education of the bachelor's degree experience at a first-rate university no doubt contributes greatly in preparing teachers of agriculture to adequately demonstrate leadership qualities and to inspire leadership in students.

Kellogg and Knapp[1] surveyed the leading agricultural colleges and found that they "are now placing more emphasis on education for long-term intellectual growth and less on how-to-do-it training in techniques for the first job." Four main trends are (1) many colleges have increased general education requirements, (2) there is a reduction in the number of technician training courses in agriculture, (3) there are fewer tightly-prescribed specialized curricula, and (4) more emphasis is placed on flexibility so that a student with the help of his counselor can work out a suitable individualized program. These changes have important implications for students preparing to teach agriculture in vocational-technical schools and departments. Academic excellence encouraged by studying in greater depth in a particular field prepares and helps a young man to be more effective in his area of occupational specialization when employed on a faculty in a school of a size sufficient to offer varied programs.

Perhaps the one most valuable pre-service professional course is student teaching. The best university teacher education departments arrange for each senior to spend the equivalent of a quarter session or a semester working in an outstanding school in the state. The experience is an internship or may be likened to cooperative work experience, usually without salary or stipend. The trainee is accepted in the school as though he were a regular staff member and he is given an opportunity to experience a cross-section of the normal teaching and other duties of a teacher of agriculture. Cooperating teachers receive special workshop training for their supervision of student teachers.

The teacher education department generally accepts considerable responsibility for inservice education of employed teachers. This is done in cooperation with the state supervisory staff and with the local school officials who supervise vocational teachers. Special attention may be given to first-year teachers; individual visits and regional group meetings are scheduled regularly in some states.

---

[1] Charles E. Kellogg and David C. Knapp, *The College of Agriculture: Science in the Public Service* (New York: McGraw-Hill Book Company, 1966), pp. 92–93.

There are incentives in most school policy statements that encourage experienced teachers to enroll in off-campus courses and to return to the university for evening, Saturday and summer courses, generally for graduate credit. It is not uncommon for one-third to one-half of the teachers in a state to hold a masters degree. While earning the degree a thesis research experience increases the teacher's competence, and may produce results worth being used in other schools. Thus, the research function of the university is extended.

University and State Programs of Research in Agricultural Education

Research is the orderly process of obtaining answers to significant questions. Inquiries worthy of systematic search for functional solutions demand a creative, imaginative approach. The dynamics of change provide basic motivational force. A thorough acquaintance with the theoretical constructs and operational trends that are taking place in vocational-technical education is antecedent to the design of research projects worth expenditure of time, talent, and funds.

The Committee on Research, American Vocational Association, opened a promotional booklet intended to encourage research with the statement:

> More important to progress in vocational and practical arts education than the establishment of specialized agencies of research—significant as that may be—is the development of a research attitude in every educator, from the state director to the local coordinator and teacher. There must be, on the part of everybody engaged in these fields, a clear recognition of the urgent need for and value of educational research.[2]

It is as necessary in the behavioral sciences as in the physical and biological sciences to recognize the complementary functions of research, development, and dissemination. Basic research is not only conducted in laboratory situations but it is most likely to be carried out by well-trained research specialists. Development, in industrial research organizations, follows basic discoveries. Schools are challenged that some developmental projects are organized to compare

---

[2] *You and Research* (Washington, D.C.: American Vocational Association, Inc., 1963), p. 3.

techniques and procedures for which basic research antecedents are lacking. There is the other complaint that the time lag between productive basic research and effective general dissemination is too long. State directors, as administrators of research programs and funds, must give these issues serious consideration. Project proposals designed by university research staff members must be cognizant of competing objectives.

With funds of Section 4-c of the Vocational Education Act of 1963 the Bureau of Adult and Vocational Research, U.S. Office of Education, has promoted establishment of a Research Coordinating Unit in each state. As qualified staff members establish relationships with universities and schools and as projects involving two or more occupational fields are initiated, the merit of the coordinating concept may be appraised.

In agricultural education there have been regional and national research coordination efforts since the 1920–1930 decade. The first publication of abstracts of studies completed prior to 1935 carried the same title as that of a continuous series of supplements. For example, Supplement No. 16, *Summaries of Studies in Agricultural Education*[3] contained 300-word abstracts of 144 selected research studies. Twenty were staff studies, 42 were doctoral dissertations and 82 were masters theses. The problems were balanced among administration, guidance, occupational opportunities and educational needs, instruction, and teacher education. Only a few used experimental design. There has been, however, in recent Supplements a steady advance from simple description to sampling survey as a research method. Analytical sampling surveys may be comparative—causal in nature; they may involve controls, randomization, and replication.

Agriculture provided the classic, and first, examples of experimental research in which analysis of variance models were used. It has been discovered that research in education may employ covariance analysis in varied experimental designs. Applications of computers to school needs is unfolding; the scope of uses will be far-reaching. Research may now be designed that, only a few years ago, would have been prohibitively laborious. But, it must not be forgot-

---

[3] *Summaries of Studies in Agricultural Education*, Supplement No. 16. OE-81002-63 U.S. Office of Education (Washington, D.C.: Government Printing Office, 1965).

ten that it is the "software," the ideas and the decision-making ability of men, rather than the "hardware," the electronic equipment, that will determine the ultimate benefits that may be obtained from effort applied to improve research designs.

The publication, *You and Research,* concluded its appeal to all vocational and technical educators to engage in research with an encouragement of cooperation:

> If one fact stands out above all others, it is that the problems of research cannot be solved by any one agency. The cooperative efforts of all groups concerned with vocational and practical arts education and its products must be focused on the problem. Labor and management groups, farm organizations, business and distributive enterprises, and homemakers' groups should be called upon for assistance. Many such groups, or individual firms, are interested in solving specific problems and are willing to work with the schools on cooperative research studies. School people must team up with other groups to find solutions which are quickly applicable so that the vocational and practical arts education of tomorrow will be the best we can conceive today.[4]

Evaluation of Local Programs of Vocational-Technical Education in Agriculture

Evaluation of an educational program is an appraisal of outcomes in terms of objectives with due consideration of the ways and means employed to attain worthwhile goals. Necessarily, then, the reader must turn back to Chapter II to re-examine the statement of objectives for vocational and technical education in agriculture. Taylor, serving as chairman of the AVA national committee, carefully differentiated *program* objectives of a school, a state, or the nation from *educational* objectives appropriate for an individual student.[5] Teachers and schools should engage in continuous self-evaluation of program objectives. State and national evaluations tend to be periodic and to rely less upon first-hand observation and more on analysis of data in formal written reports.

Evaluation in agricultural education may be traced to the early

[4] *You and Research, op. cit.,* p. 15.
[5] *Objectives for Vocational and Technical Education in Agriculture* OE-81001 U.S. Office of Education, Bulletin 1966, No. 4 (Washington, D.C.: Government Printing Office, 1965).

years of Smith-Hughes vocational programs. The product of the schools was studied in terms of job placement and advancement. It had been assumed that meeting the labor requirements of industry was *the* objective of trade and industrial education and, therefore, agricultural education should be judged on the same basis. Some years later, the ways and means approach that had been developed for evaluation of secondary schools was adapted to agriculture by a national committee and recommended to the states. Relative merits of evaluation of the *process* or of the *product* of vocational and technical education have been argued in many professional meetings and journal articles. Hensel[6] keynoted a national evaluation seminar by urging that both be considered and that criteria be developed recognizing each viewpoint. He cautioned against the possible frustrations of barriers to open and objective evaluation such as a supersensitivity to criticism, the inertia of tradition, absence of positive rewards for superiority, threatened security of personnel, and uncertainty of how to proceed. Hensel's theme was the importance of a positive attitude toward evaluation.

Principles of evaluation have emerged over the years. They need to be understood by everyone. Because the unit of school control is the local institution, usually administered by a school district and serving the people of a community, it was from this standpoint that Sutherland recommended the following:

1. Evaluations of educational programs should be made in terms of the objectives of these programs.

2. Evaluations should include assessments and appraisals of both product and process.

3. Evaluation should be a continuous process, not just a "point in time" judgment.

4. Evaluations should be made by teams composed of both professional and lay persons.

5. Evaluations of publicly supported programs should include economic factors and be concerned with input-output relationships.

6. Evaluations and appraisals should be made not only on the basis of what has been done, but also on what has not been done.

7. The major purpose of evaluation should be to provide quality control and a basis for intelligent change.

---

[6] *Evaluation and Program Planning in Agricultural Education, a Report of a National Seminar.* The Center for Vocational and Technical Education (Columbus, Ohio: The Ohio State University, 1966), pp. 9–11.

8. Evaluations should be concerned primarily, if not exclusively, with the key indicators of success or failure.[7]

In conclusion, it is relevance for the human aspirations of people who elect to commit their productive work careers to the field of agriculture that should guide teachers in this broad field as they expend their creative talents and emotional energies to promote freedom of each student to achieve his maximum potential in a sound philosophical framework. Work is a fundamental element in the development and integration of personality. It has social significance of unlimited proportions. Superior and average students readily obtain and profit from professional and technical education. For the disadvantaged, vocational-technical training is a liberating experience that lifts the person from the unemployed and impoverished to independence and human dignity. Occupational education is a right and a necessity as well as an opportunity of unbounded dimensions. It is one of the best investments that can be made by an individual, community, state, and nation.

---

[7] S. S. Sutherland, "Objectives and Evaluation in Vocational Agriculture," in *Evaluation and Program Planning in Agricultural Education, a Report of a National Seminar, op. cit.,* pp. 13–18.

Bibliography

Area Vocational Education Programs. Washington, D.C.: American Vocational Association, Inc., 1966.

Barlow, Melvin L., ed., *Vocational Education.* The Sixty-fourth Yearbook of the National Society for the Study of Education, Part I. Chicago: The University of Chicago Press, 1965.

Bender, R. E., R. M. Clark, R. E. Taylor, *The FFA and You,* Danville, Ill.: The Interstate Printers and Publishers, Inc., 1963.

Borow, Henry, ed., *Man in a World at Work.* Boston: Houghton Mifflin Company, 1964.

Brooking, Walter J., and H. N. Hunsicker, "More Skilled Agricultural Technicians Are Needed," *Agricultural Education Magazine,* XXXVIII, No. 12 June, 1966.

Byram, H. M., *Guidance in Agricultural Education.* Danville, Ill.: The Interstate Printers and Publishers, 1966.

Clark, Raymond M., and Alvin E. Oliver, "Post-High School Curriculum for the Grain, Feed, Seed and Farm Supply Industry," *Agricultural Education Magazine,* XXXIX, No. 5 November, 1966.

Farm Equipment Retailers Handbook. St. Louis, Mo.: Farm and Power Equipment Dealers Association, 1964.

Goodlad, John I., ed., *The Changing American School.* The Sixty-fifth Yearbook of the National Society for the Study of Education, Part II. Chicago: The University of Chicago Press, 1966.

Hamlin, H. M., *Public School Education in Agriculture.* Danville, Ill.: The Interstate Printers and Publishers, 1962.

Hammonds, Carsie, and Harold Binkley, *Farming Programs for Students in Vocational Agriculture.* Danville, Ill.: The Interstate Printers and Publishers, Inc., 1961.

Handbook, The Pennsylvania Young Farmers Association. Harrisburg, Pa.: Department of Public Instruction, 1965.

Hollenberg, A. H., and E. J. Johnson, *Buildings, Equipment, and Facilities for Vocational Agriculture Education.* OE-81003, U.S. Office of Education. Washington, D.C.: Government Printing Office, 1960.

Hoover, N. K., *Handbook of Agricultural Occupations.* Danville, Ill.: The Interstate Printers and Publishers, Inc., 1967.

Hunsicker, H. N., *Planning and Conducting a Program of Instruction in Vocational Agriculture for Young Farmers.* U.S. Office of Education, Voc. Div. Bul. 262. Washington: Government Printing Office, 1966.

Hutchinson, Chester S., *Your Future in Agriculture.* New York: Richards Rosen Press, Inc., 1965.

Jensen, Gale A., A. A. Liveright, and Wilbur Hallenbeck, eds., *Adult Education: Outlines of an Emerging Field of University Study.* Chicago: Adult Education Association of America, 1964.

108   BIBLIOGRAPHY

Kellogg, Charles E., and David C. Knapp, *The College of Agriculture: Science in the Public Service*. New York: McGraw-Hill Book Company, 1966.

Mason, Ralph E., and Peter G. Haines, *Cooperative Occupational Education and Work Experience in the Curriculum*. Danville, Ill.: The Interstate Printers and Publishers, Inc., 1965.

Morgan, Barton, Glenn E. Holmes, and Clarence E. Bundy, *Methods in Adult Education*, Danville, Ill.: The Interstate Printers and Publishers, Inc., 1963.

National Committee on Secondary Education, Paper Number Two, *Educating for Work*. Washington, D.C.: The National Association of Secondary School Principals, 1967.

Occupational Guidance for Off-Farm Agriculture. The Center for Vocational and Technical Education. Columbus, Ohio: The Ohio State University, 1965.

Phipps, L. J., *Handbook on Agricultural Education In Public Schools*. Danville, Ill.: The Interstate Printers and Publishers, Inc., 1966.

Planning and Conducting Cooperative Occupational Experience in Off-Farm Agriculture. The Center for Vocational and Technical Education. Columbus, Ohio: The Ohio State University, 1965.

Report of the Panel of Consultants on Vocational Education, *Education for a Changing World of Work*. U.S. Office of Education OE-80021. Washington, D.C.: Government Printing Office, 1963.

Roberts, R. W., *Vocational and Practical Arts Education*. New York: Harper & Row, Publishers, Inc., 1965.

Sanders, H. C., ed., *The Cooperative Extension Service*. Englewood Cliffs, N.J.: Prentice-Hall, Inc., 1965.

Schultz, T. W., *Transforming Traditional Agriculture*. New Haven, Conn.: Yale University Press, 1964.

Stone, Archie A., *Careers in Agribusiness and Industry*. Danville, Ill.: The Interstate Printers and Publishers, Inc., 1965.

Summary of Research Findings in Off-Farm Agricultural Occupations. The Center for Vocational and Technical Education. Columbus, Ohio: The Ohio State University, 1965.

Swanson, Gordon I., ed., *Vocational Education for Rural America*. Washington, D.C.: Department of Rural Education, National Education Association, 1959.

Venn, Grant, *Man, Education, and Work*. Washington, D.C.: The American Council on Education, 1964.

Vocational Education Bulletin No. 1, Revised 1966, *Administration of Vocational Education*. U.S. Office of Education OE-80017-A. Washington, D.C.: Government Printing Office, 1967.

You and Research. Washington, D.C.: American Vocational Association, Inc., 1963.

Index